TANKS

in detail

PzKpfw VI Ausf E & B

Panzer VI TIGER I & II

TANKS
in detail

PzKpfw VI Ausf E & B
Panzer VI TIGER I & II

TERRY J. GANDER

Ian Allan
PUBLISHING

Acknowledgements

This book could not have been produced without
the invaluable assistance of the following people:
David Fletcher, Librarian at the Tank Museum *(TM)*,
Bovington, Dorset, England, and the administrator Janice
Tate; the museum's photographer, Roland Groom *(RG/TM)*
for original images and prints from archive material.

Jasper Spencer-Smith
Bournemouth, England
July 2003

Conceived & Edited by Jasper Spencer-Smith.
Design and Illustration: Nigel Pell.
Produced by JSS Publishing Limited,
Bournemouth, Dorset, England.

Title spread: A PzKpfw VI Ausf E Tiger I loaded on a *Wehrmacht* standard
Gotha heavy transport trailer. *(TM)*

First published 2003

ISBN 0 7110 2984 9

Published by Ian Allan Publishing

an imprint of Ian Allan Publishing Ltd, Hersham,
Surrey KT12 4RG.

Printed by Ian Allan Printing Ltd, Hersham,
Surrey KT12 4RG.

Code: 0308/A3

CONTENTS

CHAPTER ONE

DEVELOPMENT

After six decades the term 'Tiger Tank' still manages
to invoke a vision of bulk and malignant might among
all with even a slight knowledge of military matters.
That vision still shows no signs of fading.

When the first Tigers appeared they created a huge problem for all Allied soldiers who faced the possibility of encountering them yet, as time was to tell, the Tiger was not invulnerable and it had its shortcomings. Even so, after the passage of years the Tiger remains one of the enduring images of tank warfare.

Origins

The origins of the Tiger tanks can be dated to 1937 when German Army planners, having laid the foundations for immediate German tank development, turned their attentions to a future *Durchbruchwagen* (breakthrough vehicle). Early considerations were centred around the premise that while the German Panzer divisions were meant to operate with force, speed and flexibility, there would be occasions when nothing less than sheer might would be necessary to break through an enemy's defences. It was therefore forecast that the required *Durchbruchwagen* would have to be heavily armoured to survive counter-measures in terms of artillery, itself being so strongly armed that it could defeat any opposing armoured vehicle.

From an early stage it was appreciated that the required tank would be heavy but, hopefully, not so heavy that the basic armoured vehicle design triumvirate of firepower, protection and mobility would not be compromised. Unfortunately for the Tiger, it was to emerge that the German national tendency towards the elephantine would create an imbalance by restricting the mobility factor, a restriction imposed by sheer weight.

Even before 1937 the German military had provided evidence of its love of the gargantuan in its search for a *Durchbruchwagen*. By the end of 1917 it had started work on a super-heavy tank intended for much the same purpose as the later 1937 version of the *Durchbruchwagen*. The objective was to develop a heavily armoured vehicle that could smash its way through Allied defences as the spearhead of the anticipated 1919 campaigns.

It appears that the Joseph Vollmer and Hauptmann Wegner engineering team, allotted the design task, was given a free hand, for the result, the *K-Wagen*, emerged as a most unlikely beast. It would have been a true leviathan, being nearly 42.65ft (13m) long, 19.7ft (6m) wide and weighing 145.7 tons (148,037.3kgs). It was meant to have been armed with four 77mm guns and six machine guns, with the armour being 1.18in (30mm)

Above:
An early production PzKpfw VI Ausf E Tiger I. Note the track links fitted by the crew to the bow plate as extra protection. The turret is fitted with the drum-shaped commander's cupola. *(TM)*

Left:
The VK4501(P) on trials at Rastenburg. This Porsche design for the Tiger did not enter production although the 90 completed chassis were used to produce the *Jagdpanzer* (SdKfz 184s) *Ferdinand*, later known as *Elefant*. *(TM)*

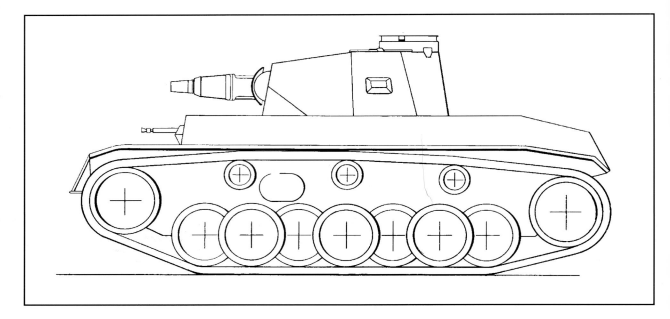

thick. Power was provided by two Daimler-Benz aero engines, each delivering some 650hp. Although the *K-Wagen* was designed to be broken down into four sections for rail transport, once assembled in a combat zone it would have been a difficult vehicle to manoeuvre or move any distance. Prospective German Army users must have regarded their future task with some trepidation.

Fortunately for them the lumbering *K-Wagen* never materialised. By 1918 the battlefield demands of World War One were stretching German industrial, human and raw material resources to breaking point. There were constant delays imposed by more urgent weapon production priorities and the non-availability of raw materials. When the Armistice of November 1918 intervened the two prototypes were still nearing completion at the Riebe-Kugellager factory in Berlin. During 1919 the two prototypes were broken up for scrap so there was no opportunity for them to demonstrate that their tactical mobility would have been essentially zero.

Durchbruchwagen

The best service the *K-Wagen* might have provided was as a semi-mobile field fortification yet thanks to there having been no opportunity to discover this the hard way,

the German tendency to consider super-heavy tanks as viable weapons persisted. The super-heavy tendency was reinforced after the *Nationsozialistische Deutsche Arbeiterpartei* (National Socialist German Workers' Party [NSDAP]) came to power in 1933, for the gargantuan, in any form, appealed to its nationalistic fervour. Anything German and impressive had to be even better when greatly enlarged, so the 1937 *Durchbruchwagen* proposal was guaranteed approval from the outset.

Even with a high measure of approval the initial development of the *Durchbruchwagen* (Dw) seems to have been marked by no particular sense of urgency. During the late 1930s the PzKpfw IV series appeared to be entirely satisfactory for any tactical task then foreseen so there appeared to be no urgent need for the type to be replaced. Henschel und Sohn GmbH at Kassel were awarded the *Durchbruchwagen* development contract, the specification setting a modest upper weight limit of 32.5 tons (32,999kgs). The result was the Dw I, followed in 1938 by the Dw II. Both prototypes were similar, both having five road wheels each side on torsion bar suspension. The installed V-12 Maybach HL 120 petrol engine was essentially the same as that employed in the PzKpfw IV series so it was appreciated these prototypes were underpowered. No turrets were mounted, their planned weight being simulated by bolted-on iron ballast.

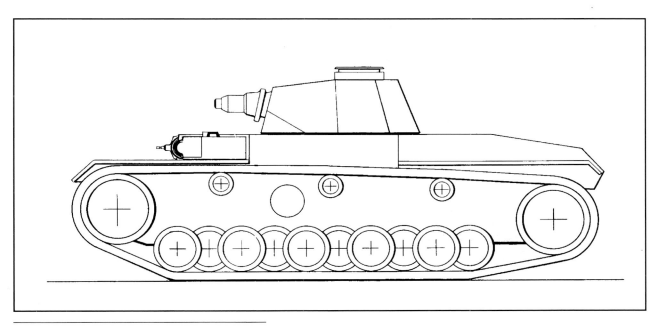

VK3001(H)

In September 1938, Henschel (H) was given an updated set of specifications, resulting in an improved version of the Dw II, the VK3001(H). The VK stood for the cover name *Vollkettenkraftfahrzeug* (fully-tracked vehicle). The VK3001(H) was also known as *Sturmwagen* (SW – assault vehicle) or as the PzKpfw VII, denoting intended introduction into service. The first of four prototypes appeared in early 1940, prior to delivery for military testing during March 1941. The VK3001(H) had seven sets of road wheels each side, the Dw II torsion bar suspension being retained. For such a heavy vehicle the armament was modest, being a short-barrelled 7.5cm KwK 37 L/24, the same as that installed in production PzKpfw IV tanks, although long-term plans envisaged a 105mm gun.

All this never happened. In May 1941 development of the VK3001(H) series was terminated in favour of a revised specification that led to the much heavier VK6501 (see below), also from Henschel. The termination of the programme was caused mainly by the appearance of thicker-armoured Allied tanks that meant whatever new German tank was intended to be produced would have to carry a larger calibre gun than had been foreseen.

Two of the VK3001 (H) chassis were later lengthened and extensively modified to carry the Rheinmetall-Borsig 12.8cm PaK44 L/55 anti-armour gun in a limited traverse assault gun mountings – the two actually saw active service on the Eastern Front during 1942 and 1943. The other two chassis were retained for various trial purposes in connection with the VK3601(H) (see below) or for driver training.

The VK6501(H), (the proposed PzKpfw VII) turned out to be an unsuccessful project. Another Henschel design venture, it was to have had a weight of about 64 tons (64,996.2kgs), mainly due to the intended overall armoured protection being 3.94in (100mm) thick. The weight entailed breaking the vehicle down in to three sections during long-distance moves, disassembling and reassembling being accomplished with assistance from an accompanying Faun crane truck. Yet the planned main armament remained the 7.5cm KwK 37 L/24 (initially at least) and the design appeared over-complicated due to features such as a traversing, hull machine gun turret. Only one prototype was manufactured, using mild steel, and tested from mid-1941. The VK6501(H) project was then cancelled.

The search for a *Durchbruchwagen* continued, but in a modified form. A rapidly changing war situation meant that by 1941 the intention was to find a viable battle tank to replace the PzKpfw IV.

VK3001(P)

From 1938 onwards the Henschel company was not alone in seeking the solution to the *Durchbruchwagen* challenge. Prototypes were also

Above:
Although the VK4501(P) was not accepted by the *Panzerwaffe*, the turret, being of superior design, was standard equipment on the Henschel-built Tiger. *(TM)*

Right:
Front view of the VK4501(P) hull produced by Krupp. This unit was used for gunnery trials. Note the marked armour thickness and plate angles. *(TM)*

ordered from the design bureau of Dr-Ing Porsche AG of Stuttgart, with the vehicle being manufactured at the Nibelungenwerke at St Valentin, Austria. The Porsche (P) prototype was officially known as the VK3001(P), although the designers knew it as the *Typ 100* or Leopard. MAN and Daimler-Benz were also asked to submit proposals but in the event these never materialised.

The Porsche design had numerous novel features, the most significant being that the two V-10 air-cooled petrol engines, also designed by Porsche, did not drive the vehicle via the usual mechanical transmission. Instead the engines drove electricity generators and the power from these drove the final drive units. The intention was that this petrol-electric transmission, a Porsche speciality dating back to heavy artillery tractors produced during the World War One years, would be more efficient and controllable than a mechanical system. Another innovation was a torsion bar suspension system with the

torsion rods located along the sides of the hull, instead of transversely.

Extensive testing demonstrated that the petrol-electric system could work but was not yet fully developed, the air-cooled engines in particular being generally unreliable. In the event the VK3001(P) programme was terminated for the same reason as for the VK3001(H), namely the realisation that the required final design would have to carry a heavier gun.

VK4501(P)

With the end of the two separate VK3001 projects in May 1941, a further series of heavier prototypes appeared. To continue the Porsche part of the story, it carried over the experience gained with its petrol-electric transmission system, the result being the VK4501(P). This

Above:
Porsche's design for the Tiger, the VK4501(P), here on trials at Rastenburg. *(TM)*

Right:
Front view of the
VK4501(H) hull
produced by Krupp.
This unit was used for
gunnery trials. Note
the marked armour
thickness and plate
angles. Note also the
hinged armour plate
for extra frontal
protection and track
protection. *(TM)*

that the reliability problems with petrol-electric transmission and air-cooled engines still persisted, to the point where the planned series production from July 1942 was terminated after only five examples had been completed.

It is not possible to go into all the many complexities of the VK4501(P) design here, it being sufficient to remark that considerable further development was necessary before the vehicle could be even considered for service. The main aspect relating to the central Tiger development narrative is that the 8.8cm gun and turret intended for the VK4501(P) was carried over to the rival Henschel VK3601(H) design.

To complete the VK4501(P) saga, the design eventually evolved into the ill-starred *Panzerjäger* (tank hunter) or *Jagdpanzer* known as *Ferdinand* and later as the *Elefant* (SdKfz 184). Ninety of these were built, their fate deserving of a completely separate account away from the Tiger development sequence. That continues with the Henschel VK3601(H).

VK3601(H)

Once heavily armoured tanks such as the British Matilda and French Char B-2 had been encountered by the Germans in mid-1940 it was considered that a gun capable of defeating 3.94in (100mm) of armour at a range of 1,640.4yd (1,500m) would be required on future German battle tanks. The appearance of the Soviet T-34 in 1941 could only emphasise this requirement, the corollary being that the up-gunned tank would have to be sufficiently armoured against a similar weapon. The prospect of tanks weighing well over 49.2 tons (49,999.4kgs) then became a reality. While many considered such weight increases to be acceptable, or even laudable due to their propaganda potential, many German *Waffenampt* (ordnance) officers did not and sought to find some means of keeping combat weights within reasonable limits.

One immediate solution to the gun requirement was to utilise the 8.8cm gun mentioned above. This would result in a tank weighing 56 tons (56,999.3kgs). Many *Waffenampt* personnel considered that 39.4 tons (39,999.5kgs) would be a more convenient upper limit so guns with calibre lengths of 60, 70 or 75mm were considered. The smaller calibre guns would require smaller turrets and turret rings, the hull

was to carry a tank gun derivative of the 8.8cm anti-aircraft guns then in production by Krupp of Essen (and others) as the *8.8cm FliegerabwehrKanone 18, 36 oder 37* (8.8cm FlaK 18, 36 or 37), the three models differing by changes to the barrel construction and the fire controls. To carry the tank version of this gun (the *8.8cm KampfwagenKanone 36L/56* [8.8cm KwK 36L/56]), Porsche designed a turret that was also to be manufactured by Krupp AG at Essen. As the VK4501(P) was expected to weigh approximately 56 tons (56,999.3kgs) the Porsche design bureau considered that its petrol-electric transmission system was the only way to reliably handle the vehice weight involved.

Such was the rush to get the new up-gunned tanks into the field that series production of the Porsche vehicle, together with the turret, was ordered at the same time as the VK4501(H) prototype was rolled out in April 1942. This rush to production was premature as it soon transpired

Right:
The Henschel
VK4501(H) which
was to become the
production Tiger
on trials. Note the
circular-shaped ballast
placed on the turret
ring. The vehicle is
being inspected by
a high-ranking Nazi
party official. *(TM)*

width could be reduced accordingly and thus weight could be saved. The problem was that to develop such guns to the point where they could penetrate 3.94in (100mm) of armour at 1,640.4yd (1,500m) posed considerable technical difficulties. A 7.5cm gun with a barrel 70 calibres long was considered at one stage, the gun later being installed on the Panther tank series but at the time the armament quandary was under discussion it was not yet ready for service. Something more immediate was required.

One possible, although unorthodox, solution was proposed by Fried. Krupp AG at Essen. One of its technicians, a Doktor-Ing Gerlich, had carried out considerable research regarding high-velocity taper-bore guns firing special flanged or 'skirted' projectiles. The idea was to employ the propellant charge to drive a full-bore projectile down the barrel as normal. As the projectile travelled towards the muzzle the calibre gradually decreased, pressing the skirts down and back into the projectile body. As the barrel diameter decreased the propelling pressure remained the same the projectile velocity accelerated, greatly increasing the resultant muzzle energy. When this extra kinetic energy was combined with an extremely dense armour-penetrating core the result was a significant increase in armour penetration. A lighter calibre gun could then, on paper at least, meet the armour penetration specification.

Krupp developed the Gerlich principle to the point where it appeared on a series of three towed anti-tank guns issued for field service. One of these, the *7.5cm PanzerabwehrKanone 41* (7.5cm PaK 41), had its initial 75mm bore reduced to 55mm at the muzzle. Developed in tandem with this towed gun was a tank version known by the design designation of *Gerät 0725*. It was this gun that was intended to be installed in the Henschel VK3601(H), the competitor to the VK4501(P). This would limit the combat weight of the Henschel design to just over 39.4 tons (39,999.5kgs). Firing tests were to demonstrate that the *Gerät 0725* projectile weighing 5.48lb (2.48kgs) could penetrate 5.87in (149mm) of armour set at 0° at 1,640.4yd (1,500m), with a muzzle velocity of 3,970ft/sec (1,210m/sec).

It was not to be, for there was a drawback regarding the *Gerät 0725*. To ensure the taper-bore gun was to perform as required, the projectile's armour-penetrating core had to be tungsten. As early as 1940 supplies of the raw materials needed to produce tungsten and its alloys had been cut off

from Germany by naval blockade. Stocks accumulated before 1940, therefore, had to be strictly set aside for machine tools, for without machine tools all war production would soon cease. The *Gerät 0725* was therefore doomed almost as soon as it appeared. Approximately a total of only 150 examples of the towed 7.5cm PaK 41 were manufactured and issued to the *Wehrmacht*. Once the ammunition already manufactured for those guns was expended there would be no further supplies.

This posed the German ordnance authorities with a considerable predicament. By early 1942 the prototype intended to carry the taper-bore gun, the Henschel 3601(H) had already been built. The corresponding VK4501(P), although already selected for mass production, was soon displaying its many technical shortcomings to the point where, even in early 1942, it appeared that the Porsche design would ultimately prove unsatisfactory. To comply with the pressing demands of army units and to get the new tanks into the battlefield ready for the planned 1943 offensives, the only immediate solution was to place the Krupp 8.8cm gun and turret intended for the VK4501(P) onto the Henschel VK3601(H) hull.

This required some rapid redesigning of the VK3601(H), the sole prototype of which had to be largely abandoned, although many of its features were retained for the new vehicle, including the eight sets of interleaved road wheels on each side. Henschel was required to limit its changes to hull-related aspects and a more powerful engine and transmission as the combat weight was an anticipated 56 tons (56,999.3kgs). As the main hull changes had to be introduced to accommodate the wider turret ring, the box-sectioned hull of the VK3601(H) had to be altered to a broad T-shape, the outer edges of the T then overhanging the tracks as two rows of panniers.

The Porsche gun turret was already in production by Krupp by that stage (April 1942) and required little modification once the Henschel hull had been extensively modified. The overall hull width had to be increased from 10.3ft (3.14m) to 12.14ft (3.7m), a width factor that was to cause rail transport problems later in service use. The VK4501(H), known as the *PanzerKampfwagen* (battletank) *Ausführung* (model) E (*SonderKraftfahrzeug* [special purposes motor vehicle] *181*), or SdKfz 181-PzKpfwVI-Ausf ETiger I.

Production of this new combat vehicle commenced at the Kassel factory during July 1942.

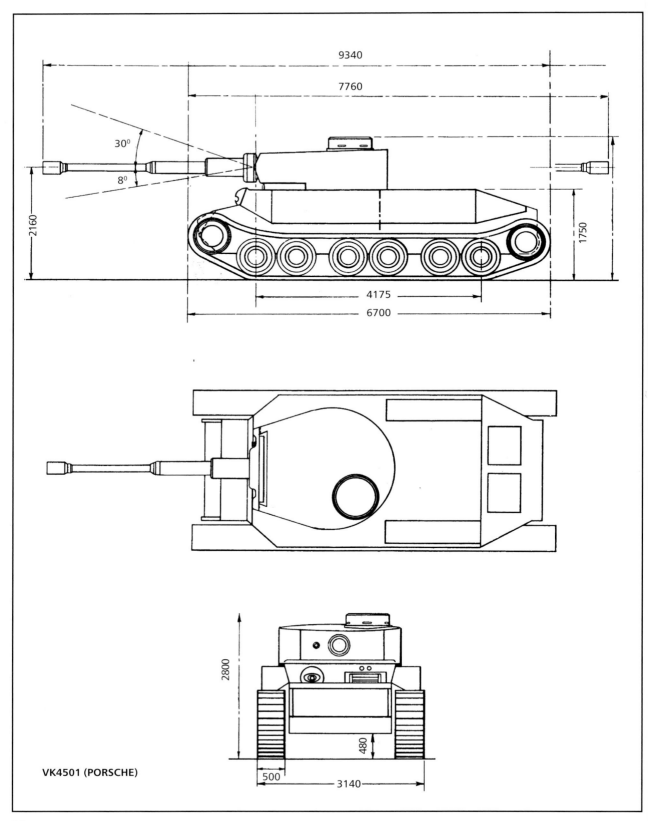

VK4501 (PORSCHE)

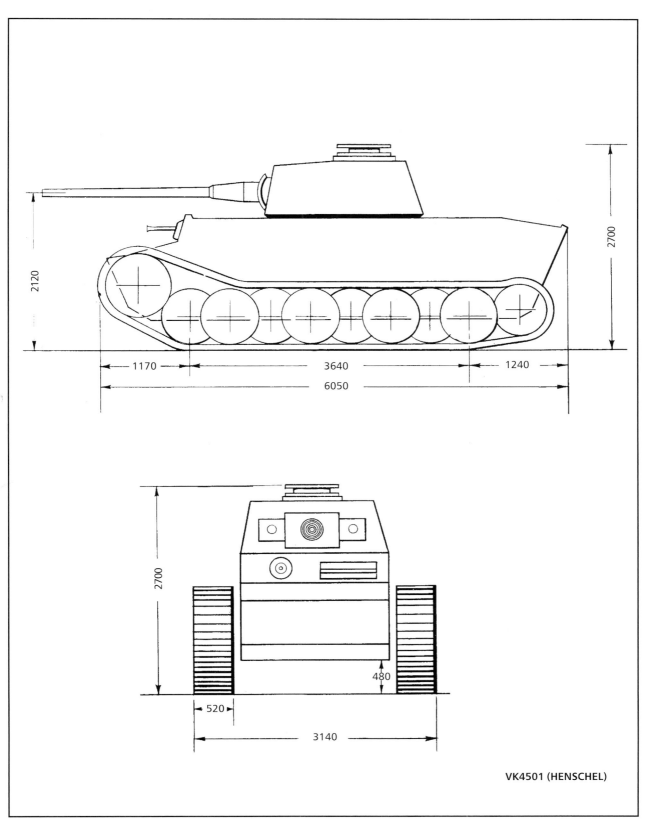

2120

2700

1170   3640   1240

6050

2700

480

520

3140

VK4501 (HENSCHEL)

CHAPTER TWO

TIGER I

Despite its overall size and mass the Tiger I was conventional in overall layout. It incorporated many attentions to fine detail to the extent that it was difficult and expensive to manufacture.

One of the most significant points regarding the overall design and build of the Tiger I was that virtually every aspect had to be designed from new. Very few components or construction methods could be carried over from existing designs as the size and weight of the Tiger I presented their own special-to-type problems.

Another overall point regarding the Tiger I, and German tanks in general, was that the standard of workmanship throughout was of very high quality. No chance was missed to utilise the best technical approach or standard then possible, or apply fine finishes or other refined manufacturing procedures, the result being a superb example of precision military machinery capable of absorbing the most dreadful punishment in battle.

It also appears that little consideration was given to cost or speed on the production line. Each Tiger I required considerable factory and other resources to manufacture, the raw materials for a single example of the hull being sufficient to manufacture at least two complete PzKpfw IV tanks. The number of manufacturing man-hours demanding the attention of skilled personnel was also considerable.

The end result was a significant cost per vehicle. A single Tiger I, without armament or other combat equipment and accessories, cost the huge sum of *Reichmarks* (RM)250,800. By contrast, a contemporary PzKpfw IV Ausf F2, manufactured to the same exacting standards as the Tiger I, cost RM 103,462. It is interesting to note that a single example of a completed Tiger I shipped to Japan via Bordeaux in February 1944 was billed at RM 645,000.

All this has to be set against the example of the contemporary Soviet T-34, where speed and ease of manufacture was paramount and the general standard of rushed completion was just adequate, except on vital components. The end result was still an excellent and practical combat machine and the Soviets were to have far more of them than the Germans could ever build.

Hull

Although imposing, the overall form of the Tiger I was basically simple. The hull was an immensely strong box structure, much of the strength being derived from the thickness of the flat, high-quality armour plates used in the construction of both the hull and superstructure.

Above:
Officers of the *Panzerwaffe* inspect the production line at Henschel's facility in Kassel. The Tiger I was produced at this factory from August 1942 to August 1944 with a total of 1,350 delivered out of the 1,376 which had been ordered. *(TM)*

Left:
The sides of the distinctive horseshoe-shaped turret were formed from one piece of armoured steel in the giant hydraulic presses at the Krupp works, Essen. *(RG/TM)*

More strength was obtained by the stepping or interlocking of many of the armour plate joints prior to welding, the result being a much stronger bond than that produced by just welding together connecting surfaces. Wherever possible the plates were single-piece components, the hull floor, for instance, being largely formed from a single plate 1.03in (26mm) thick. Not only did the single plates make manufacturing that much easier but they added to the protection provided and also to hull and superstructure strength.

To emphasise the protection factor, the armour plates were 3.94in (100mm) thick at the front, 3.15in (80mm) at the upper sides, and 2.4in (60mm) at the lower sides. The rear plate was 3.23in (82mm) thick while the flat hull top was 1.03in (26mm) thick. To utilise the example of the contemporary PzKpfw IV Ausf F2 again, the thickness at the best-protected points was 1.97in (50mm).

Where possible, the armour plates were set vertically around the hull and superstructure, presenting a completely flat face to incoming projectiles. On many vehicles extra protection was added by the application of *Zimmerit*, anti-magnetic paste liberally spread over external surfaces using a combed applicator. This was a field task, the paste drying to a hard ribbed surface that discouraged the adhesion of manually placed, shaped charges secured by magnets to an armoured vehicle, an armour-defeating technique quickly learned by Soviet tank-killer squads after the Germans themselves introduced such effective anti-tank measures.

To emphasise the overall box structure, the hull and superstructure formed a single unit, the superstructure being extended sideways over each track. The hull was divided into four internal compartments. At the front, two compartments housed the driver (on the left) and the bow machine gunner (on the right), the latter also doubling as the radio operator. The radio carried was a standard *FunkSprechGerät* (FuSprGer) 5, a 10-Watt transmitter operating in the 27,200 to 33,300Kc/s frequency band with a voice range of about 2,187yd (2,000m). Command versions of the Tiger I carried extra radios.

Each forward compartment had its own overhead entry hatch with a fixed-vision episcope facing forward. Behind them was the main combat compartment housing, apart from the main armament, the commander, gunner and loader. Behind this main compartment was the engine compartment, the two separated by a solid bulkhead.

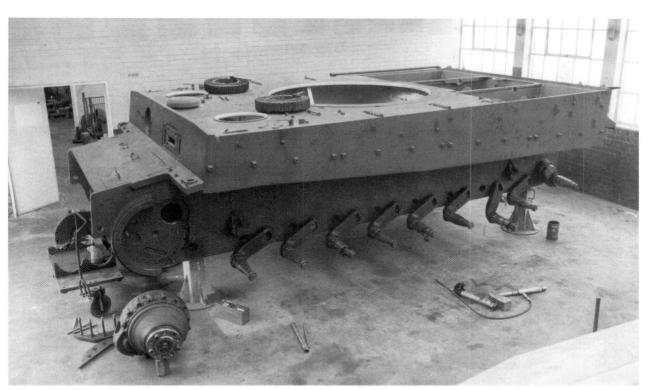

Turret

For the period, the turret was remarkable in its size and the way it was largely formed from a single curved, rolled armour plate. The gun mounting presented few deviations from then current practice. The turret sides overall horseshoe shape was formed at the Krupp works by one of the large hydraulic presses that were among the prime manufacturing assets in use at Essen. The turret was 3.23in (82mm) thick, all-round frontal protection being afforded by a cast, one-piece gun mantlet. This was 4.33in (110mm) thick at its deepest point, bordered by two 3.94in (100mm) thick bars. By 1945 it was common practice for extra protection to be added by suspending spare track lengths around the turret sides.

Roof protection was provided by another single plate, this time 1.02in (26mm) thick and recessed into the curved sides. From the turret centre line forward the roof was inclined downwards to permit the breech to recoil when fired at the angles of depression required during tank warfare. The commander had a vision and access cupola to the left of centre (looking

forwards). This access point was shared with the gunner while the loader had his own access roof hatch on the right. On early Tiger I production examples two wedge-and-chain-type sub-machine gun ports were provided in the turret rear sides to provide a measure of close-in protection against infantry tank-killer squads. The port set into the right rear turret wall was later converted into an ammunition reloading hatch. This hatch could also serve as an escape hatch for the loader. A sliding shutter could close the driver's main vision port in the superstructure front plate. For extra vision to the outside, both the gunner and loader had vision ports in the turret side walls.

The commander's cupola underwent some changes. It was initially a low drum-shaped structure with five protected vision slits around the circumference. In another measure introduced to simplify production, the same cupola as fitted to Panther tanks fitted with six episcope-type vision ports, was phased in on the production lines. Mounted on the turret rear were one or two stowage panniers for the crew's kit and other items, although these were sometimes not fitted.

By armoured vehicle standards the turret interior was relatively spacious. Much of the

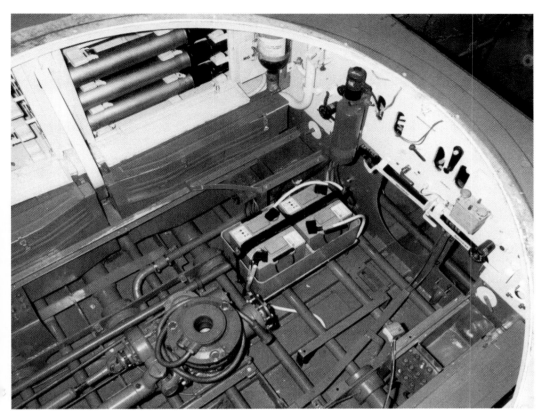

Left:
The fighting compartment with the turntable removed. In the centre is the rotary base power take-off unit, on which the turntable rotated, which supplied hydraulic power to the traversing motor. Note the ammunition stowage bin. *(RG/TM)*

internal volume was occupied by the gun breech that almost reached the rear wall when on full recoil, thus virtually dividing the interior in two. Consistent with previous German tank designs, the turret had a floor that rotated with the turret, while the loader was provided with a rear-facing seat for when use travelling. Ready-use ammunition was stowed in bins each side of the combat compartment, with more rounds stowed under the turret floor or next to the driver.

The turret was traversed on ball bearings through a full 360° under hand or hydraulic power control. Fortunately for many Allied tank crews the rate of powered traverse was slow due to the gearing ratio dictated by the weight of the turret, so slow that faster Allied tanks could move before the

Below:
Panzerwaffe gunners being trained in the operation of the Tiger's turret, Jutland, Denmark. (TM)

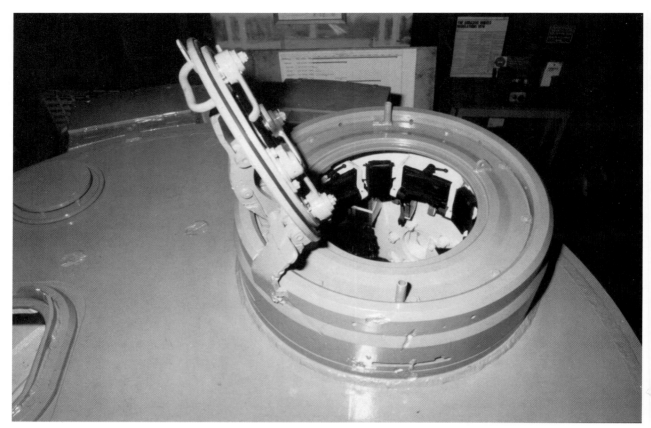

Above:
The commander's cupola on the Tiger I followed the design of earlier German tanks with five vision ports fitted with *Ersatzgläser* (synthetic glass) blocks. *(RG/TM)*

Right:
The gun loader's position was in the right-side of the turret and was provided with a rectangular-shaped hatch fitted in the one-piece turret roof. *(RG/TM)*

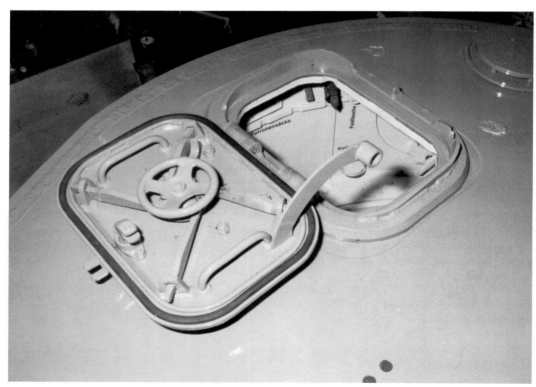

Above and left:
Tracks on the Tiger I were made up of 96 links each side. Cast from manganese steel they were held together by a single pin retained by a clip. Combat tracks were 28.53in (724mm) wide and the smooth-faced transport tracks were 20.49in (520mm) wide. At the top is a link showing the idler and road wheel guide lugs and to the left is the link showing the surface contact side. *(TM)*

Right:
The belly plate on the Tiger was made from one piece of metal measuring 15.85ft (4.83m) long, 5.92ft (1.8m) wide and 1.02in (26mm) thick to assist with the rigidity of the hull. The 24 road-wheels each side are clearly shown. Note there is no belly escape hatch for the crew, only engine bay access plates. *(TM)*

Left:
One of the four (two front, two rear) hydraulic shock absorbers fitted in the hull. Note also the Argus disc brake for emergency steering and main braking. *(RG/TM)*

Left:
Torsion bar suspension in the hull of the Tank Museum's Tiger I. *(RG/TM)*

Left:
Fitting a torsion bar. Note the splined end for mounting the road wheel suspension lever. *(RG/TM)*

Tiger's gun could be brought to bear. Inside the turret the hydraulic drive unit was located in the centre of the turret floor, with connections so arranged that the turret drives could be disconnected using a single dog clutch on the drive shaft. This simple expedient allowed, when necessary, the turret to be lifted off the superstructure without having to worry about numerous hydraulic pipes and associated parts. Manual control of the turret involved hard labour, the gunner having to turn a handwheel 720 times to effect a full (and slow) 360° traverse.

Tracks & Suspension

At this point in the narrative the construction and drive descriptions overlap, due to the turret ring dimensions. The Porsche-designed turret was originally intended for the VK4501(P) which had the hull designed to accommodate the turret ring internal diameter of 5.87ft (1.79m). On the Porsche design the overall vehicle width was tailored to 11ft (3.38m), just sufficient to allow it to be within the confines imposed by the width of the railway wagon necessary for long-distance moves which, in its turn, was limited by railway tunnel dimensions and other such considerations. When

the Porsche turret and turret ring were hurriedly transferred to the Henschel VK4501(H) during early 1942, the turret ring could not be so easily accommodated. The best width that could be achieved was 12.24ft (3.73m), outside the railway wagon width restrictions. To alter the hull to anything less would have imposed intolerable delays in getting the tank into service.

The only way this travelling by rail problem could be quickly resolved was by introducing a process of laboriously removing the eight outer road wheels (four from each side) and the installation of special narrow tracks. The hull sills over the tops of the tracks also had to be removed, while the outer extremities of the track front dust flaps were hinged. These measures reduced the overall width to 10.33ft (3.15m) so rail transport was then no longer a problem, other than the task of wheel removal and making the transition from wide to narrow tracks before each railway move. Before combat it was required that the wide tracks were refitted, once the outer road wheels had been refitted.

Each track was formed from 96 links, made from cast manganese steel. Combat tracks were 28.53in (724mm) wide and weighed 2.85 tons (2,900kgs), the smooth-faced narrow tracks for transport being 20.49in (520mm) wide. The drive sprocket was at the front of the vehicle with

Left:
As with all German tanks track tension was adjusted at the idler wheel. Note the guide lugs on the track links. *(RG/TM)*

Left:
The drive sprocket was cast from manganese steel and machine finished. Note the front roadwheel has been removed. *(RG/TM)*

Above:
Maybach (Norddeutsche Motorenbau Gmbh, Berlin) produced engines for most types of German tanks. The V-12, HL 210 TRM P45 was a very large engine as can be seen from this rebuilt example being fitted in the Tank Museum's restored Tiger I. The designations were as follows: TRM–*Trockensumpf-schmierung mit Schnappermagnet*, dry sump lubricant with impulse magneto; P–*Panzermotor*, tank engine; HL – *Hoch-leistungsmotor*, high-performance engine. (RG/TM)

a rear idler wheel being used to make adjustments to track tension. Access to the tension adjusting points was from inside the hull rear plate. The combat width tracks were very necessary for they spread the weight of the vehicle over a wider area, preventing any degradation of performance imposed if narrower tracks were involved.

Two types of road wheel were used during the Tiger I's service career. The first production models had interleaved dished steel wheels with rubber tyres. There were 24 of these each side, carried on eight trailing suspension arms. To save space inside the hull the independently sprung torsion bars utilised for the suspension were arranged so that the trailing arms faced to the rear on the left (facing forwards) and to the front on the right. In order to make production easier and reduce costs, during January 1944 the dished wheels were replaced on the production lines by steel tyred and internally sprung wheels of the same diameter. On the very last production Tiger Is the outer row of road wheels was left off altogether as the steel wheel design could handle heavier loads than its dished equivalents. These wheels were also installed on late-production Panther and Tiger II tanks.

Between them the Tiger's interleaved road wheels and the torsion bar suspension provided a smooth and steady ride for the crew, even over comparatively rough terrain. Their one drawback, shared by other German vehicles with interleaved wheels, was that under Eastern Front winter conditions snow or mud which became packed between the wheels could freeze solid to the extent that the vehicle could not move under its own power. Any attempt to move with the offending mass still in place usually resulted in a broken track.

Power

When considering the Tiger I engine pack and drive train it has to be remarked that the vehicle was under-powered. The all-important fomula of firepower, mobility and protection was thus compromised. The protection and firepower factors were there in abundance but moving them around was a different matter.

The first production Tiger Is had an engine developed specifically for them by Maybach of Berlin, the company that produced most of the German tank engines from 1935 until 1945. The first Tiger engine, the V-12 Maybach HL 210 TRM P45 was a water-cooled petrol engine with a capacity of 21,330cc, developing 650bhp at 3,000rpm. Despite this being a powerful engine by

contemporary standards it was soon apparent that the Tiger I was seriously under-powered but there were engine compartment volume and other technical limitations that prevented the installation of a larger, more powerful power unit. The best that could be achieved was the replacement of the original engine by a larger capacity 23.88-litre unit, the HL 230 P45, again a V-12 water-cooled petrol engine. This increased the power available to a nominal 700bhp at 3,000rpm. To save scarce raw materials the larger engine had the HL 210 P45's aluminium cylinder block replaced by one manufactured in cast iron and bored out to 23.88 litres (23,880cc).

Even this power increase was not enough. The Tiger therefore suffered from inherent poor performance, with the top road speed being no more than 23mph (37km/h). Travelling across rough terrain speed was reduced to around 12.43mph (20km/h). Both speeds were far below those of other, smaller tanks of the time so many potential Allied targets were able to escape to cover before a Tiger could attack.

The engine also had a high fuel consumption rate. Allied reports mention a figure of 2.75 gallons for every mile (12.5ltr per 1.61km). As the fuel capacity of the four fuel tanks provided, two each side of the engine compartment, was

approximately 125gal (568ltr), it can be deduced that the operational range of a Tiger I was limited and refuelling stops had to be frequent, especially when travelling off roads. The German logistic planning figures were 121.2 miles (195km) and 68.4 miles (110km) respectively.

Cooling

The two engine cooling radiators were at the rear, each with its own cooling fans, the water being circulated by a centrifugal pump. Two sets of air pre-cleaners were located on the rear hull plate, two each side of the twin exhaust pipes. For operations under dusty conditions, such as in North Africa or over the Russian steppes, an additional air pre-cleaner system, known as the *Feifel*, was located over the top of the engine compartment plates. This system was omitted on late production examples.

Considerable attention was devoted towards enabling the Tiger I to negotiate water obstacles, as few bridges could withstand the weight of the vehicle. The engine compartment was therefore sealed, as were other vulnerable points. It was then possible for the vehicle to traverse water obstacle up to about 4ft (1.22m) deep but by adding a total

Above left:
A complete V-12 Maybach HL 230 TRM P45. The engine was fitted with two Bosch JGN 6 R12 impulse magnetos for ignition. *(RG/TM)*

Above:
The same engine with two of the four Solex 52 JFF2D down-draught carburettors removed. Clean air to these was drawn through multi-element air filters. *(RG/TM)*

Above:
Engine cooling fans
drew air through the
radiators which in turn
were protected by
engine deck-mounted
air filters. *(RG/TM)*

Right:
The fan/radiator
assembly shared
a bay with the fuel on
each side of the engine
compartment. *(RG/TM)*

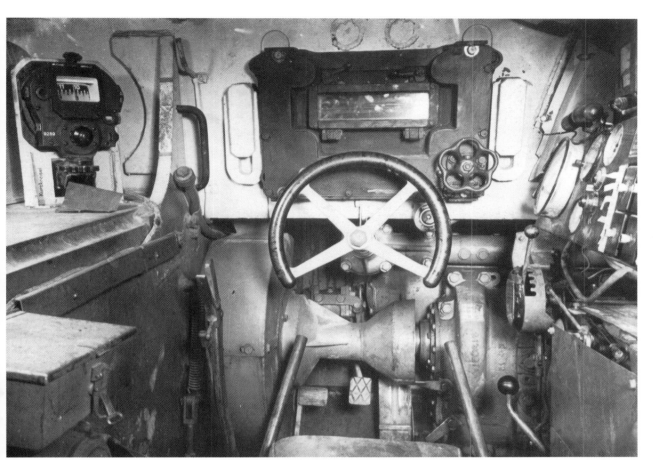

Above:
The Tiger was the first German tank to be fitted with wheel steering for the driver. The levers each side of the driver's seat were for brake steering. Note the *Schutzgläser* (bullet-proof glass) vision port and (left) the gyro compass. *(RG/TM)*

Left:
Engine instruments and preselector gear change control for the driver. Note the spare *Schutzgläser* blocks stowed above the panel. *(RG/TM)*

submersion kit the vehicle could travel through water up to nearly 13.1ft (4m) deep. To facilitate this each vehicle had special features incorporated into the basic design.

All hatches opened outwards and had rubber sealing surfaces, the turret/hull interface being sealed by an inflatable rubber ring. When submerged, air was drawn into the vehicle through a snorkel tube erected over the rear of the vehicle. Thoughtfully, incoming air was first circulated through the crew compartments before being passed to the engine compartment. For submersion the radiator fans were disconnected and the machine gun ports and main gun mantlet were plugged or sealed, the machine guns being dismounted. Should any water enter the interior a bilge pump was provided in the main compartment.

It was intended that this submersion system would allow the vehicle to remain submerged for up to $2^1/_2$ hours. Understandably, few soldiers ever tested this figure for the submersion kits were rarely, if ever, used operationally. Late production Tiger Is had this complicated and expensive to produce system removed, their crews relying purely on the basic wading capability of the tank.

Transmission

Power was taken forward from the engine along a transmission drive shaft under the main compartment floor to the gearbox located to the right of the driver. This was a Maybach type 401216 Olvar pre-selector type with eight forward and four reverse gears fitted into a small unit together with power take-offs for the turret hydraulic drive and the bilge pump. Controls were light and the gearbox was easy to operate. From the gearbox drive was transmitted to the drive sprocket on each side, at the front, via spur reducing and epicyclic gears inside the sprockets.

The Henschel-designed steering unit was based on the British Merritt-Brown type, which was fully regenerative and continuous, and was mounted transversely in the bow of the tank, the steering drive going to a final reduction gear in each sprocket. The driver was provided with a steering wheel that was light and easy to turn thanks to hydraulic assistance. Control levers actuating Argus disc brakes on each drive shaft were used whenever the emergency steering system had to be employed. This system also acted as the main braking system under foot pedal control.

Specifications - Tiger I

Crew:	Five (commander, driver, main gunner, bow machine gunner/radio operator, loader)
Weight in combat:	circa 56.1 tons (57,000kgs)
Length:	27.72ft (8.45m)
Width:	combat tracks, 12.24ft (3.73m)
	narrow tracks, 10.34ft (3.15m)
Height:	overall, 9.61ft (2.93m)
Track:	combat tracks, 9.28ft (2.83m)
	narrow tracks, 8.96ft (2.73m)
Track width:	combat tracks, 28.53in (724mm)
	narrow tracks, 20.49in (520mm)
Ground clearance:	17.73in (450mm)
Max speed, road:	23mph (37km/h)
Fuel capacity:	125gal (568ltr)
Range, road, max:	121 miles (195km)
Fording:	standard tank, 4ft (1.22m)
Vertical obstacle:	2.59ft (790mm)
Trench crossing width:	12.96ft (3.95m)
Gradient:	35°
Engine:	21,330cc V-12 Maybach HL 210 TRM P45 water-cooled petrol developing 650bhp at 3,000rpm or 23,880cc Maybach HL 230 P45 V-12 water-cooled petrol developing 700bhp at 3,000rpm
Transmission:	Maybach Olvar type 401216 hydraulically operated preselector gearbox with eight forward and four reverse gears
Carburettors:	Four Solex type S2JFF2D
Ignition:	Two Bosch type JGN6R12 impulse magnetos
Steering:	regenerative
Suspension:	torsion bar
Electrical system:	12V
Armour, front:	3.94in (100mm)
side:	2.44in (62mm)
top and floor:	max, 1.02in (26mm)
turret sides and rear:	3.23in (82mm)
Armament:	1 x 8.8cm KwK 36 (L/56)
	2 x 7.92mm machine guns
	1 x Beretta or MP40
	6 x 90mm NebelKanone 39 (smoke dischargers)
Optical Equipment:	1 x TZF 9b or c
	1 x KZF 2
	1 x SF14Z (sf)

Note: TZF: *Turmzielfernrohr* (Turret sighting periscope)
KZF: *Kugelzielfernrohr* (Ball-mounting sighting telescope)
SF: *Scherenfernrohr* (Scissors-type telescope)
sf: *Selbstfahrlafette* (Self-propelled carriage [SP gun])

CHAPTER THREE

ARMAMENT – TIGER I

The main combat asset of the Tiger I was its powerful gun capable of knocking out Allied tanks at extreme ranges using advanced ammunition. This main gun was backed up by machine guns.

It has long been reported that the main gun, the *8.8cm KampfwagenKanone 36* (8.8cm KwK 36) was a variant of the *8.8cm FliegerabwehrKanone* (FlaK) series. Pedantically, this is not strictly true for the KwK 36 had little in common with the 8.8cm anti-aircraft guns other than having identical ballistics and firing the same ammunition. The tank and anti-aircraft guns differed by their methods of construction in many ways, not the least of them being that the KwK 36 barrel was manufactured in one piece and contained within a thin steel jacket. The semi-automatic Hotchkiss-type breech block opened vertically downwards and the muzzle fittted a muzzle brake to alleviate the recoil stresses on the mounting.

The 8.8cm KwK 36 was, according to legend, yet another brainchild of Adolph Hitler, apparently inspired by a demonstration of the 8.8cm anti-aircraft gun during 1938. It was manufactured by Krupp and had a barrel 56.1 calibres long, firing fixed, one-piece ammunition (the projectile and metal case containing the propellant were loaded joined together in one piece). The cost of a new 8.8cm KwK 36 was a nominal RM 18,000.

The ammunition fired from the 8.8cm KwK 36 was as shown below:

Of these the two main types carried by Tiger Is in combat were the *8.8cm PanzergranatePatrone 39* and the *8.8cm PanzergranatePatrone L/4.5*. The *8.8cm HohlladungGranate 39* was rarely carried, while the projectile for the *8.8cm Panzergranate Patrone 40* had a tungsten carbide core. Scarcity of tungsten meant the latter ammunition could not be produced in quantity, even if it did have a superior performance, and all production of it ceased during 1943. The *8.8cm Panzergranate Patrone 39* projectile could penetrate the specified

	Projectile weight	Muzzle velocity	Type
8.8cm PanzergranatePatrone 39	22lb (10 kgs)	2,657.5ft/sec (810 m/sec)	armour-piercing
8.8cm PanzergranatePatrone 40	16lb (7.27 kgs)	2,998.7ft/sec (914 m/sec)	armour-piercing
8.8cm PanzergranatePatrone L/4.5	21lb (9.54 kgs)	2,690.1ft/sec (820 m/sec)	high explosive
8.8cm HohlladungGranate 39	17lb (7.65 kgs)	1,968.5ft/sec (600 m/sec)	hollow charge

Above:
The Tiger I mounted the powerful *8.8cm KampfwagenKanone 36* (8.8cm KwK36) which was developed from the *8.8cm Fliegerabwehr-Kanone* (FlaK anti-aircraft gun). *(TM)*

Left:
A dummy Tiger constructed from wood and canvas to confuse the enemy. Many were used as shown here in Italy and in Normandy. From a distance or from the air they appeared very realistic. *(TM)*

Above:
This Tiger I Ausf E was captured in Tunisia during World War Two. The vehicle is now in the Tank Museum, Bovington, Dorset, England and has been fully restored. *(TM)*

3.94in (100mm) of armour at 1093.6yd (1,000m).

An equal number of armour-piercing and high-explosive ammunition appears to have been the usual combat allotment. Bearing in mind that most training was carried out using high explosive only (saving the more expensive armour-piercing rounds for combat) the following production table, by year, indicates KwK 36 ammunition production priorities. It has to be remembered that the 8.8cm KwK 36 was fitted only on the Tiger I. The Tiger I production totals are also provided here for comparison purposes.

	1942	1943	1944
8.8cm PanzergranatePatrone 39	21,200	324,800	394,400
8.8 cm PanzergranatePatrone 40	800	8,900	–
8.8 cm PanzergranatePatrone L/4.5	14,100	1,392,200	459,400
Tiger I production	78	649	623

Although they were otherwise identical to their FlaK equivalents, rounds for the KwK 36 differed by having electrical (instead of percussion) primers. Total ammunition stowage was 92 rounds, all stored horizontally in unarmoured sheet metal bins.

On the Tiger I the 8.8cm KwK 36 L/56 was mounted so that the barrel, located 4.23in (107mm) to the right of the fore and aft centre line, had workable elevation limits of from -4° to +11°, traverse being a full 360°, as with the turret. The traversing power controls were operated by the gunner using his right foot to depress control pedals. Elevation was controlled manually by the gunner using a handwheel turning a rack and pinion arc to his right. The handwheel carried the trigger bar, firing being accomplished via an electric firing pin. After recoil the vertical sliding breech block opened downwards to eject the spent case into a canvas bag holding up to 10 cases. Whenever possible the bag contents were thrown from the turret to prevent the accumulation of corrosive fumes that could affect crew breathing.

When seen from the side, about a quarter of the barrel length extended beyond the front of the hull, the length from the muzzle brake to the

mantlet being about half that of the tank itself. This meant the gun was muzzle heavy so its forward weight was balanced by a coil spring in an internal cylindrical housing to the right of the gun, located behind the loader's seat. Some of the imbalance was caused by the double-baffle muzzle brake weighing 123.9lb (56.2kgs). Despite the effort involved, the muzzle brake was sometimes removed for long moves and carried inside the turret

For aiming, the gunner was provided with an optical sight. This could be either a Leitz of Wetzlar binocular *Turmzielfernrohr 9b* (TZF 9b turret sighting telescope) on early production models or the monocular TZF 9c (on late production models). Both had 2.5 magnification and a range scale marked up to 4,374.4yd (4,000m). For the few occasions when the main gun would be used to deliver indirect fire at unseen targets the barrel elevation was set using a clinometer positioned next to the gunner. The commander could point the gun towards a potential target independently of the gunner by using his own set of auxiliary manual controls and a sighting vane in the forward-facing episcope on the cupola. A *70cm Entfernungsmesser* (EM-rangefinder) could be mounted on the turret roof.

Machine Guns

The Tiger I carried two machine guns, both *7.92mm Maschinengewehr 34* (7.92 mm MG34). One was in the turret, to the right of and co-axial to the main gun. The other was in the hull right front. The co-axial gun was aimed using the gunner's usual optical sight graticule (although with a separate range scale marked up to 1,968yd [1,800m]) and fired by a foot pedal. The ammunition feed was arranged so that 150-round ammunition belts could be inserted only from the left-hand side. Access for loading was reported to be difficult.

The bow machine gun was mounted in a hemispherical ball mounting arranged so that the inherent breech heaviness was counter-balanced by a tension spring. This MG34 had the butt stock removed and firing was by a manual trigger. Elevations limits were -7° and +20°, with the traverse 15° left and right. The sight was the *Kugelzielfernrohr 2* (KZF2-ball-mounting sighting scope) with 1.75 magnification, as employed in other similar German armoured vehicle and fortification mountings.

Above:
The breech block mechanism was of the Hotchkiss-type, a standard feature on all German tank guns. Note (to the right) the coaxial MG34 machine gun. *(TM)*

Above:
Gunner's controls. Note the TZF 9b binocular sighting telescope, turret position indicator and the gun elevating wheel with firing trigger. *(TM)*

Right:
The hull MG34 machine gun and KZF2 sighting scope. Note the ammunition bags stowed in the hull side locker. *(TM)*

On late-production models with the Panther-pattern commander's cupola there was an external *Fliegerabwehrschussgerät* (anti-aircraft ring mounting) for a further MG34, or the later MG42, for air defence, although it appears this option was not always used. There was stowage provision for up to 38 belts of 7.92mm ammunition, making 5,700 rounds in total. Of these, 17 belts were stowed in the main combat compartment.

Other Weapons

A standard fitting on all Tiger I tanks was two banks of three electrically fired *90mm NebelKanone 39* smoke-screen canister dischargers, one bank each side of the turret. These were 'one shot' measures as no spare smoke canisters were carried for reloading.

At least one 9mm MP38 or MP40 sub-machine gun was carried in each vehicle for dismounted use and also for close in defence against infantry when fired from one or other of the two firing ports in the turret rear. Late-production Tiger Is had only one firing port. The official ammunition allotment for one sub-machine gun was 192 rounds for loading into 32-round magazines. Also carried was a 27mm flare pistol with 24 rounds.

Perhaps the most unusual of all weapons carried on the Tiger I were the single-shot, anti-personnel *Minenwerfer* (S mines) installed around the superstructure. There could be up to five of these, intended for use against enemy infantry tank-killer squads operating close to the vehicle. These were pre-loaded and fired upwards and outwards, the projectile being a cylindrical, thin-walled metal canister 5in (128mm) long and 4.14in (105mm) in diameter. Once about 4.9ft (1.5m) from the tank the projectile detonated, scattering three hundred and sixty .39in (10mm) diameter steel balls in all directions. These devices were not always carried.

Above:
Alongside the breech block and coaxial machine is the loader's position. Note the rear-facing seat and the vision port placed in the side of the turret almost behind the loader. *(TM)*

CHAPTER FOUR

VARIANTS – TIGER I

Despite front-line demands for battle tanks the Tiger I
was also used as the basis for several variants,
not the least of which was the outlandish Sturmmörser.
Less drastic were the Tiger I command tanks.

The combat version of the Tiger I was the *Panzerkampfwagen VI Ausf E* (SdKfz 181) with two close variants, the *Panzerbefehlswagen VI Ausf E* (SdKfz 267) and the *Panzerbefehlswagen VI Ausf E* (SdKfz 268). Both were command tanks that differed from the battle tank by carrying an extra radio for communicating with higher command, rather than just with local field formations. A total of 84 of these command models were listed, all apparently delivered during 1944, although some were probably conversions of existing vehicles.

The SdKfz 267 carried the usual *Funk-SprechGerät 5* (FuSprGer 5) radio installation plus the *FunkSprechGerät 8* (FuSprGer 8), the standard divisional-level radio link within Panzer formations. The SdKfz 268 carried the usual FuSprGer 5 installation plus the *FunkSprechGerät 7* (FuSprGer 7), used for ground to air communications. In both of these command versions the space taken up by the extra radio meant that ammunition stowage had to be reduced. On both, the number of 8.8cm rounds was reduced to 63 (32 APCBC and 31 HE) and the number of 7.92mm rounds to 4,050.

Radio Equipment	
FuSprGer 5:	10-Watt transmitter and ultra short-wave receiver on frequency band 27,200 - 33,300K/cs.
FuSprGer 7:	Standard ground to air communications radio on 42,100 - 47,800K/cs.
FuSprGer 8:	30-Watt transmitter and medium-wave receiver 1,120 - 3,000K/cs.

Sturmmörser

The most-modified Tiger I variant was probably the most outlandish armoured vehicle ever to grace the military scene. It was the *38cm RW61 auf Sturmmörser Tiger*, usually known simply as the *Sturmmörser*, heavy assault mortar. This beast had its origins in the 1942 fighting for Leningrad and Stalingrad when stout structures acted as fortresses' difficult to demolish. One proposed demolition solution was to modify a Porsche *Elefant* chassis by adding a tortoise-like armoured carapace that could be driven

Above:
A captured intact *Sturmmörser Tiger* (also known as Sturmpanzer VI) being towed by a *Bergepanzer Panther* (Bergepanther) at a British Army testing establishment in England. *(TM)*

Left:
The muzzle of the *38cm RacketenWerfer 61* (RW61 – rocket launcher) mounted in the *Sturmmörser Tiger*. Around the muzzle ring are 31 holes, bored down to the breech to allow the escape of firing gases. This weapon could fire a 760.6lb (345kg) projectile to a range of 4,374.4yd (4,000m). *(TM)*

Above:
Alkett of Berlin-Spandau rebuilt 18 old Tiger chassis with steel roadwheels, modified suspension and superstructure from Brandenberger Eisenwerke. Total vehicle weight rose to 68.9 tons (69,999.2kg). *(TM)*

Right:
An American soldier measures the ammunition for the *Sturmmörser Tiger*. The high-explosive *38cm RaketenSpreng-granate 4581* (RS-rocket propelled mortar) was loaded into the breech by the small crane device shown. *(TM)*

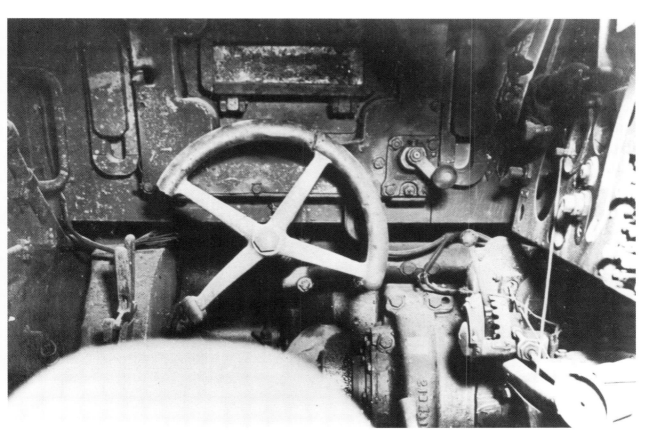

Above:
The driver's position on the *Sturmmörser Tiger* had the same controls as the Tiger tank although the area was more cramped. *(TM)*

Left:
The breech mechanism on the RW61 was of the sliding type operating a crank and geared rack, loading being accomplished with the externally mounted small crane. *(TM)*

Right:
US troops examining a damaged *Sturmmörser Tiger*. The mortar could be fired at 0° to an elevation of 85°; it could also be traversed 10° to the left and 10° to the right. A ball-mounted machine gun was also fitted in the glacis plate, which was 5.91in (150mm) thick. Side armour was 3.15in (80mm) thick. The vehicle carried a crew of five and 12 projectiles in a very cramped interior. *(TM)*

Left and below:
A sequence showing trials with *Schnorkel* equipment on a PzKpfw VI Ausf E Tiger. The experimental fully-waterproofed tank is fitted with early-type equipment which allowed a depth of around 10ft (9.85m) to be negotiated. Production Tigers without *Schnorkel* could traverse water obstacles only to a depth of 4ft (1.22m). Later rear-mounted *Schnorkel* equipment allowed the Tiger to travel underwater to a depth of 13.1ft (4m). *(TM)*

Above:
The turret of a *Bergepanzer Tiger* recovery vehicle was an 'in the field' conversion of an Ausf E gun tank. Note the blanked-off port for the main gun in the mantlet. *(TM)*

into heavy structures to demolish them. This would have been the *Rammtiger* (dozer tank) but that idea got no further than models.

Instead, the *Sturmmörser* was conceived. It was produced by taking a turretless Tiger I hull and adding a massive armoured box superstructure. Inserted in the sloping front plate and behind a massive mantlet was a *RaketenWerfer* (RW-rocket launcher) designed by Rheinmetall-Borsig, the *38cm Raketen-Werfer 61*. This launched the massive *38cm RaketenSprenggranate 4581* high-explosive warhead rocket weighing about 760.6lb (345kgs) to a maximum range of 4,374.4yd (4,600m), although it was intended that operational ranges would be much less. The rocket shell was originally devised as an anti-submarine weapon. The launcher resembled a short-barrelled, large-bore gun and was breech loaded, the rocket exhaust produced at firing being directed forward through a ring of 31 holes around the gun muzzle.

Development of the *Sturmmörser* began in August 1943, the first prototype appearing in October that year. Production was ordered but for some reason did not commence until August 1944, by which time any need for such a vehicle had long passed. Alkett of Berlin-Spandau was provided with 18 used Tiger chassis which were refurbished and updated, mainly by the provision of all-steel wheels and changes to the suspension. These were very necessary for the addition of the armoured superstructure from Branden-berger Eisenwerke at Kirchmäser and the Rheinmetall-Borsig RW61 launcher brought the final combat weight up to nearly 68.9 tons (69,999.2kgs). As the early production V-12 Maybach HL 210 TRM P45 650hp engine was retained it meant the *Sturmmörser* was so ponderous that its tactical mobility was almost zero. Maximum road speed was supposed to be 25mph (40km/h) but it is doubtful if such a speed was ever achieved. Off roads the vehicle must have been rendered virtually immobile.

The frontal armour of the *Sturmmörser* superstructure was 5.91in (150mm) thick, and 3.15in (80mm) for the sides. Despite its height and bulk, the superstructure interior was cramped as racks were provided for the carrying of 12 rockets (plus another carried in the launcher). Reloading was via a circular hatch in the superstructure rear, with the assistance of a small jib crane. An extra loader was sometimes added to the usual crew of five to assist in handling the rockets. A single 7.92mm MG34 machine gun was fitted in a ball mounting in the glacis plate for close-in defence.

The last *Sturmmörser* was completed in December 1944. Although there was no viable combat role for them by then, all were issued to three specially formed *Sturmmörser* companies and deployed in small, scattered numbers, supposedly in a last-ditch defensive role. It appears that all of them were soon put out of action. One wonders why they were ever built, other than as an example of the NDSAP love for the gargantuan, or perhaps to keep Hitler happy.

Others

During 1944 three examples of the *Bergepanzer Tiger* armoured recovery vehicle were produced, probably as in the field workshop conversions. The conversion involved removing the main gun and installing a winch inside the turret. The winch cable was directed forward via a short crane secured to the turret front. One of these vehicles was captured in Italy.

The Tiger I was supposed to form the basis of other variants, none of which actually appeared for one reason or another, the main reason being that production of the Tiger I was terminated in favour of the Tiger II.

Above:
It is thought that only three *Bergepanzer Tigers* were converted, one being captured in Italy, 1944. Note the hand-operated, geared winch mounted on the turret rear. The turret is fitted with the Panther type of commander's cupola with seven episcopes and anti-aircraft gun mounting ring. *(TM)*

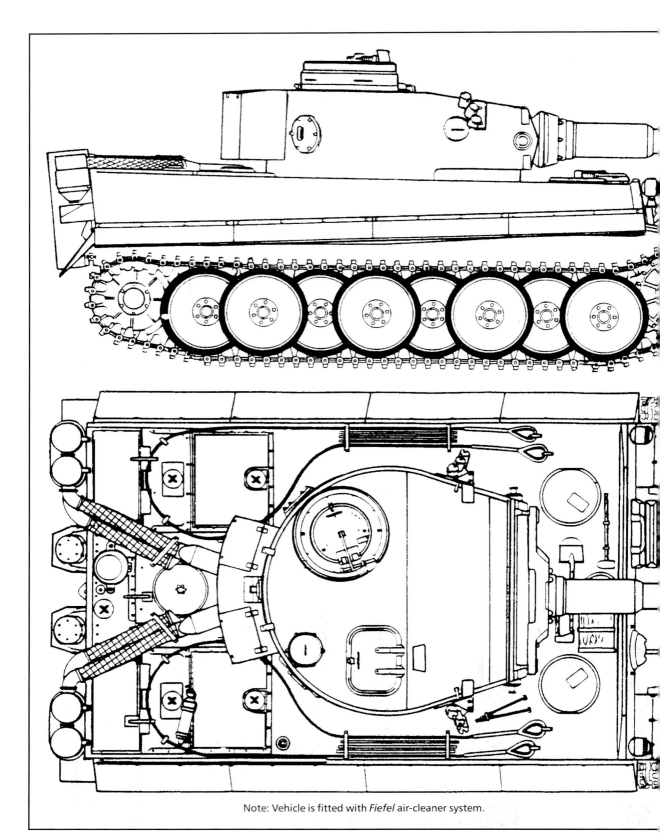

Note: Vehicle is fitted with *Fiefel* air-cleaner system.

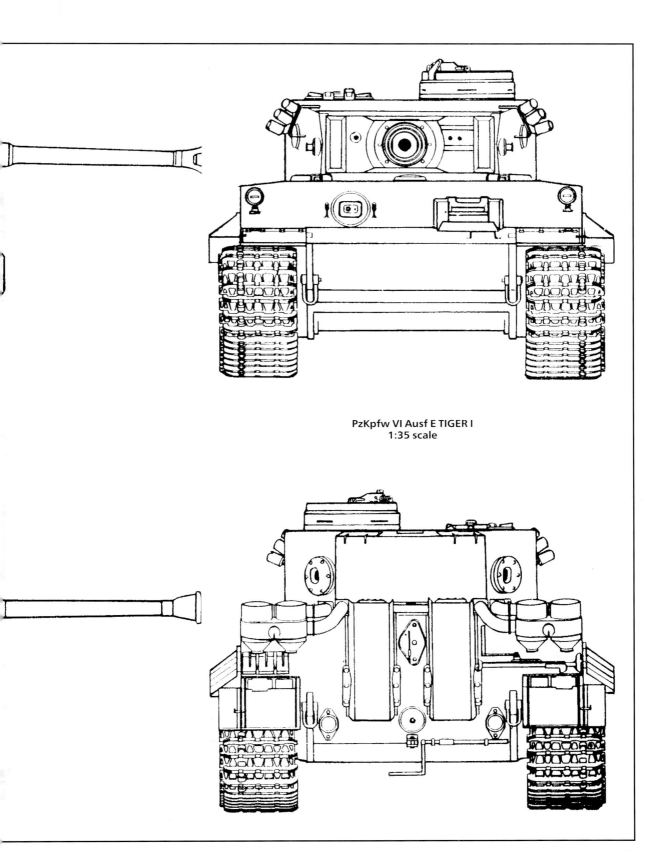

PzKpfw VI Ausf E TIGER I
1:35 scale

CHAPTER FIVE

DEVELOPMENT – TIGER II

Combat experience demonstrated that the Tiger I could
be improved upon, not least in armoured protection.
The development path was far from straightforward,
resulting in two approaches that finally merged.

Almost as soon as the Tiger I was entering production consideration was being given to its replacement. The specifications for such a vehicle were issued as early as August 1942, the general outline being that the vehicle had to be everything the Tiger I was already, but improved all round. The gun was to be more powerful, and the armoured protection had to be improved, mainly by the incorporation of sloping armour plates for the superstructure but also by increasing frontal armour to 5.91in (150mm).

The introduction of sloping armour had been dictated by the appearance of the Soviet T-34, protected as it was by an angled plate super-structure. The sloping plates not only considerably increased the thickness of armour presented to incoming projectiles, but also served to deflect solid armour-piercing projectiles. It was not long before the design was adopted completely by German designers for the Panther series and specified for what would become the Tiger II.

Once again, both Porsche and Henschel were asked to enter design submissions. Porsche had already been investigating the possibilities of its so-called *Typ 180*. The proposed armament was to be a 105 or 150mm main gun but the project was rejected. Porsche staff then proposed the

VK4502(P), retaining their preferred petrol–electric drive system but this time with the engine compartment at the front and the turret at the rear. The armament proposed was the 8.8cm KwK 43 L/71, of which more later.

On paper the VK4502(P) appeared to have considerable promise, especially as it seemed that many of the earlier petrol-electric technical problems had been eliminated. Unfortunately for Porsche it was the electrical part of the system that caused the cancellation of its project. By 1944 the scarcity of some critical raw materials was acute. The electrical part of the Porsche transmission demanded a considerable amount of copper for the motors and conductors, just at a time when the German war economy had insufficient quantities to hand. The VK4502(P) programme was therefore terminated, but not before turret production had already commenced at Wegmann AG of Kassel.

VK4503 (H)

At the same time that Porsche made its initial proposal, Henschel proposed its VK4503(H).

Above :
A PzKpfw VI (Sdkfz182)
Ausf B Tiger II fitted
with the Porsche-
designed turret and
8.8cm KwK 43 L/71
gun. The first 50
production Tiger IIs had
this turret before the
Henschel design was
adopted as standard
equipment. *(TM)*

Left:
A captured vehicle
compound in France
with a Tiger II alongside
its predecessor, on the
left, a Panther. Note the
close similarity in the
shape of the glacis
plate on both vehicles.
The Tiger II has the
Porsche turret. *(TM)*

This was essentially a Tiger I with the required sloping armour, to the extent that the final result resembled an enlarged Panther tank. With the Porsche design eliminated, the main production contract therefore passed to Henschel. Mock-ups were ready by October 1943, with production planning in progress by January 1944. The first few examples were delivered to the *Panzerwaffe* at the end of February 1944.

The Henschel VK4503(H) was known by different designations and names. Officially it was the *Panzerkampfwagen VI Ausf B* (*Sonder Kraftfahrzeug 182*) or *Panzerkampfwagen Tiger Ausf B*. To many German soldiers it was the *Königstiger* (King Tiger), to Allied troops it was known as the Royal or King Tiger. Others knew it simply as the Tiger II.

Full series production was partially delayed by an understandable demand for the German armoured vehicle industry to adopt a higher degree of component and sub-system commonality than had previously been achieved. Not only would this simplify and speed production generally but it would make component inter-changing more possible under field conditions. This policy was applied to the Tiger II and the proposed Panther II, the next development step in the Panther

Below :
Porsche's design- VK4502(P)- for the improved Tiger had petrol-electric drive, as did its unsuccessful predecessor, the VK4501(P). Although this design was not chosen, 50 turrets which had been produced were fitted to the first Henschel-built Tiger IIs. *(TM)*

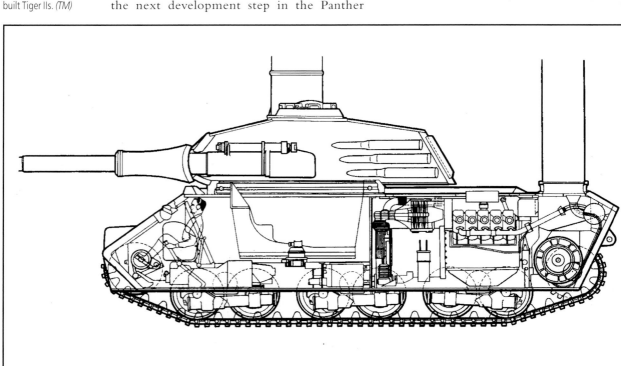

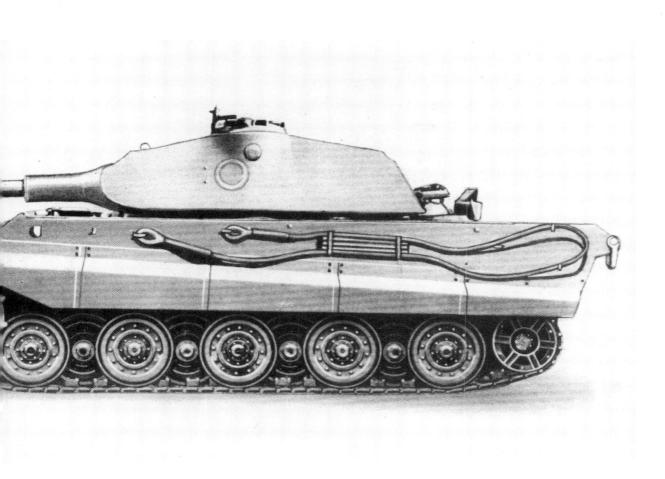

series. The most noticeable result was that the same steel tyred and internally sprung wheels were installed on both vehicles, while the commander's cupola was the same as that fitted to the Panther. Both also shared the same engine installation. By the time all the necessary inter-change plans had been completed about three valuable production months had been lost. Throughout this early Tiger II period, series production of the Tiger I and Tiger II took place side by side, the Tiger I finally being phased out during August 1944.

An optimistic production rate was planned for the Tiger II. By April 1944 this was scheduled to be 12 per month. This would increase to 100 per month by August 1944, rising to 140 each month from November 1944 onwards. Such totals were never achieved for many reasons, not the least being an increasing supply shortfall in both raw and finished materials, and a general disruption of the Third Reich's industrial and transport infrastructure under constant Allied bomber attack and land advances. The best production

figure ever achieved was 84 in the month of August 1944.

One early set-back occurred after an enemy bombing raid on Kassel during October 1943, when not only were manufacturing preparations disrupted but also many skilled personnel were killed. The raid meant that only one prototype had been completed by the end of 1943. During 1944 a total of 376 Tiger IIs were produced and a further 112 in early 1945. The last production examples could not even be delivered. The final total of 490 was far short of the numbers planned.

As the Porsche turrets were already in production by the time Henschel was awarded the production contract, they were installed on the first 50 production Tiger IIs. By December 1943 it had been realised that these turrets had a shortcoming in that the curved area under the gun mantlet formed a shot trap for incoming fire. Henschel was therefore asked to design this feature out of its planned turrets and this was duly accomplished. After the 50th Tiger II left the factory all Tiger IIs had the wider, slab-sided Henschel turret.

Above :
An early PzKpfw VI Ausf B Tiger II fitted with the Porsche turret. The chassis was developed as the Henschel design-VK4502(H)- for the improved Tiger. The Porsche turret was abandoned as the curved area under the mantlet proved to be a shot trap for incoming fire. *(TM)*

Right:
US Army personnel recovering a Henschel-turreted Tiger II. To many German soldiers the vehicle was known as *Königstiger* (King Tiger) and to Allied troops as Royal or King Tiger. The Allied tank in the photograph is an M4AI (75mm) Sherman. *(TM)*

CHAPTER SIX

TIGER II

The Tiger II followed much the same lines as the Tiger I, only there was more of it. The general layout and construction remained the same, as did the usual high standard of German workmanship and attention to detail.

The general layout and construction of the Tiger II remained the same as the Tiger I, as did the usual high standard of German workmanship and attention to detail. The one glaring omission was the lack of attention given to mobility. The German love of the leviathan was bearing its fateful fruit. Once again, firepower and protection were favoured to the detriment of mobility.

The main weakness of the Tiger II was that the same V-12 Maybach engine fitted in the Tiger I fitted in to the new tank. As had already demonstrated, this engine could not deliver sufficient power to move a Tiger I, except at a ponderous pace, the heavier Tiger II was even slower. A combat-ready Tiger I weighed 53.15 tons (53,999.4kgs). The Tiger II weighed 68.7 tons (69,671.52kgs) yet the same 700hp engine installation was meant to power both. The Tiger II was therefore even more cumbersome and under-powered than the Tiger I, with all the tactical and other disadvantages this entailed.

Needless to say, the Tiger II was more expensive to produce than the Tiger I. Being more demanding in raw materials and manufacturing resources, the Tiger II cost RM 321,500 without armament or other equipment.

The main armament alone cost an additional RM21,000.

Construction

The internal layout of the Tiger II was much the same as for the Tiger I other than there was more internal space and better access to more crew escape hatches than before. The driver and bow machine gunner/radio operator both had their own overhead access hatches and they also had improved access to the main combat compartment behind them. In return, the turret crew also gained access to the driver and bow machine gunner hatches.

One of the main features of the Tiger II was its sloped homogeneous steel armour that, as mentioned elsewhere, afforded better protection for the vehicle and crew. The sloping armour effects were amplified by the front glacis plate being 5.91in (150mm) thick, set at 40° from the vertical. The sloping lower hull was 3.94in (100mm) thick. Side and rear armour was 3.15in (80mm) while the top and floor armour thickness were increased to 1.58in (40mm). As

Above:
Tiger II fitted with the production Henschel turret, which was more roomy and less vulnerable to incoming fire. The commander's cupola is of the Panther pattern. *(TM)*

Left:
A white flag flutters from the cupola of this Tiger II (with Henschel turret) which has been captured by US troops during fighting in the Battle of the Bulge. *(TM)*

Above:
The Tank Museum's Tiger II. This view clearly shows the multiple curves of the Porsche-designed turret. *(RG/TM)*

Right:
The Panther-type cupola fitted to late Ausf E Tigers and Tiger IIs. Note the armoured cover for the turret ventilator fan. *(TM)*

before, the armoured surfaces involved were, wherever possible, formed by large single plates interlocked before welding. The armoured steel came from locations as far apart as the Skoda-Werke at Pilsen, Czechoslovakia and Krupp AG at Essen. Coatings of *Zimmerit* were usually applied at the factory.

No provision was made for any form of submersible wading gear on the Tiger II. Instead the hull was carefully sealed, during production, to allow water obstacles up to 5.25ft (1.6m) deep to be safely negotiated.

Turret

As mentioned earlier, the first 50 Tiger IIs had the Porsche turret. This required extra attention during manufacture in that numerous curves had been introduced into the overall shape, including the shot-catching curve under the mantlet. Another curve accommodated the offset Panther pattern cupola, the latter retaining the seven episcopes as fitted on late models of the Tiger I.

The need for such curves did little to ease or speed production so the Henschel turret, the main production type, did away with such finesse as it was designed to be wider. There was then no longer any need for the armour to curve by the cupola and at the same time armour protection became even thicker.

On the Henschel turret the front armour was 7.17in (182mm) thick, sloped at 10° from the vertical. On the Porsche turret it was 3.94in (100mm) at the thickest point and 3.15in (80mm) elsewhere. The Henschel turret sides were 3.15in (80mm) thick, as was the roof armour. Added frontal protection was provided by a massive, one-piece, cast-steel gun mantlet with a rounded *Saukopfblende* (Pig's Head) profile.

As there was no external turret stowage, set into the rear of the turret was a rectangular hatch that opened outwards and downwards. It served mainly as an ammunition reloading point and also another escape hatch. Thanks mainly to the wider turret this hatch was larger on the Henschel turret than on the Porsche design. Set into the centre of the hatch was a sub-machine gun firing port.

Above:
A *Panzer-Abteilung* (tank battalion) of Henschel-turreted Tiger IIs being inspected by their commander in tank No. 300. *(TM)*

Above:
A Henschel turret assembly for a Tiger II loaded on a railway truck, possibly a spare for delivery to a maintenance unit. *(TM)*

Right:
At the top is the Porsche turret, mounting the 8.8cm KwK43 L/71 fitted with a single-sleeve barrel. At the bottom is the same gun (with a two-piece barrel) mounted in the Henschel turret. Note the different styles of mantlet. *(TM)*

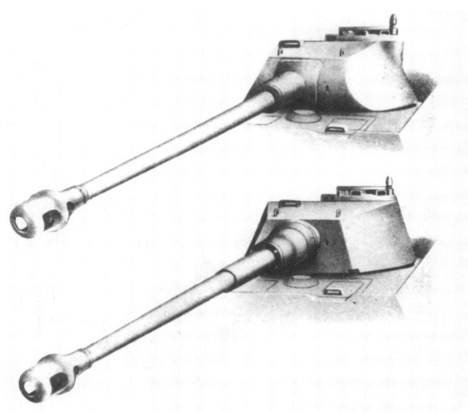

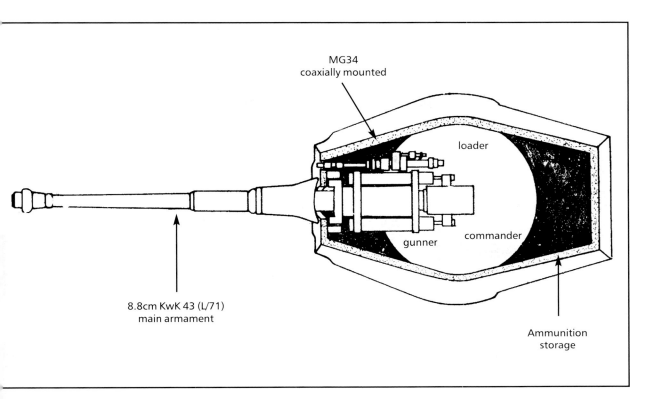

MG34
coaxially mounted

loader

commander

gunner

Ammunition
storage

8.8cm KwK 43 (L/71)
main armament

Engine

As mentioned above, the automotive power source for the Tiger II was a V-12 Maybach 23,880cc HL 230 TRM P45 water-cooled petrol engine. This provided a nominal power output of 700hp at 3,000rpm, although it appears that 650hp was the best that could usually be achieved. The abnormally high fuel consumption rate remained. Constantly under heavy loads, mechanical breakdowns were frequent and engine life short.

Another carry-over from the Tiger I was the transmission, the Maybach Olvar type 401216B hydraulically-operated gearbox fitted with eight forward and four reverse gears. Final drive and steering mechanisms were the same as those fitted to the Tiger I.

The full fuel load of approximately 189.2gal (860ltr) was distributed in seven tanks. There were two tanks each side of the engine, one each side of the combat compartment and one to the rear of the engine. The logistically planned road range was 105.64 miles (170km) and 74.6 miles (120km) off road. In practice these ranges were much shorter.

Wheels and Tracks

The Tiger II suspension continued to use torsion bars, this time with nine axles each side. Each axle carried two interleaved steel tyred and internally sprung wheels, the internal springing on rubber bushes. The design and construction of these wheels made them more able to carry the weights involved than the earlier Tiger I wheels and there was less chance of them becoming jammed with frozen snow or mud.

The travelling width restrictions that beset the Tiger I were carried over to the Tiger II. For rail transport a special set of narrow tracks had to be fitted and the side mud guards and wheel covers over the sides also had to be moved. There was no need to remove the outer wheels. As before the tracks were formed from cast manganese steel links, each complete track requiring 96 track links. Combat tracks were 31in (787mm) wide and weighed 3.3 tons (3,350kgs), the narrow tracks being 26in (660mm) wide. As before, the wide combat tracks were very necessary to spread the load, especially for when traversing soft terrain but changing from the transport to the combat tracks (and back) was laborious and time consuming.

Above:
A section through the Henschel turret showing equipment and crew positions. The stowage area at the rear of the turret carried 22 rounds of ammunition (11 each side of the recoil space), 30 other rounds were carried in stowage bins around the sides and floor area of the vehicle.

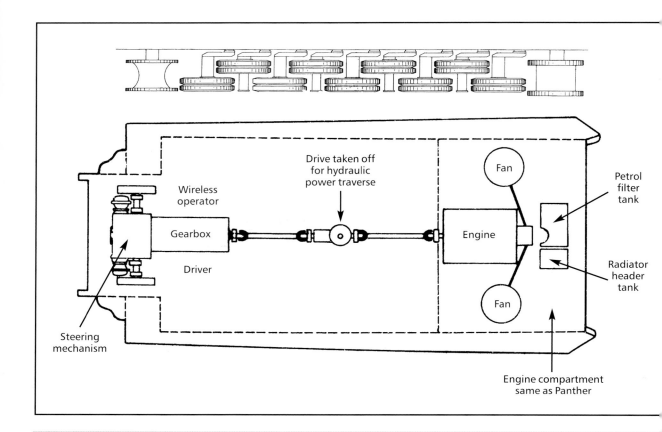

Figure labels:
- Drive taken off for hydraulic power traverse
- Wireless operator
- Gearbox
- Driver
- Steering mechanism
- Fan
- Fan
- Engine
- Petrol filter tank
- Radiator header tank
- Engine compartment same as Panther

Specifications - Tiger II

Crew:	Five (commander, driver, main gunner, bow machine gunner/radio operator, loader)
Weight in combat:	68.7 tons (69,800kgs)
Length:	33.76ft (10.29m)
Width:	combat tracks, 12.33ft (3.76m)
	narrow tracks, 11.90ft (3.63m)
Height:	overall, 10.10ft (3.08m)
Track:	combat tracks, 9.28ft (2.83m)
	narrow tracks, 8.96ft (2.73m)
Track width:	combat tracks, 31in (787mm)
	narrow tracks, 26in (660mm)
Ground clearance:	19.5in (495mm)
Max speed, road:	nominal, 25.5mph (41km/h)
Fuel capacity:	with reserve tank, 189.2gal (860ltr)
Range, road, (max):	ca 105.64 miles (170km)
Fording:	5.25ft (1.6m)
Vertical obstacle:	2.79ft (850mm)
Trench crossing width:	12.96ft (3.95m)
Gradient:	35°
Engine:	23,880cc V-12 Maybach HL 230 TRM P45 water-cooled petrol developing 700bhp at 3,000rpm

Transmission:	Maybach Olvar type 401216B hydraulically-operated, preselector gearbox with eight forward and four reverse gears
Steering:	regenerative
Suspension:	9 torsion bars
Electrical system:	12V
Armour, front:	5.9in (150mm)
side:	3.15in (80mm)
top and floor:	max, 1.58in (40mm)
turret front:	7.1in (180mm)
turret sides:	3.15in (80mm)
Armament:	1 x 8.8 cm KwK 43 L/71 gun
	2 or 3 7.9 mm MG34 machine guns
	1 x *Nähverteidigungswaffe*
	(Breech-loaded smoke mortar)
Optical Equipment:	1 x TZF 9d
	1 x KZF 2
	1 x SF14Z (sf) later replaced by HWF 3
	1x EM 1.6mR (from 03/45)

Note: HWF: *Handwinkelfernrohr* (Hand periscope)
       EM: *Entfernungsmesser* (Rangefinder)

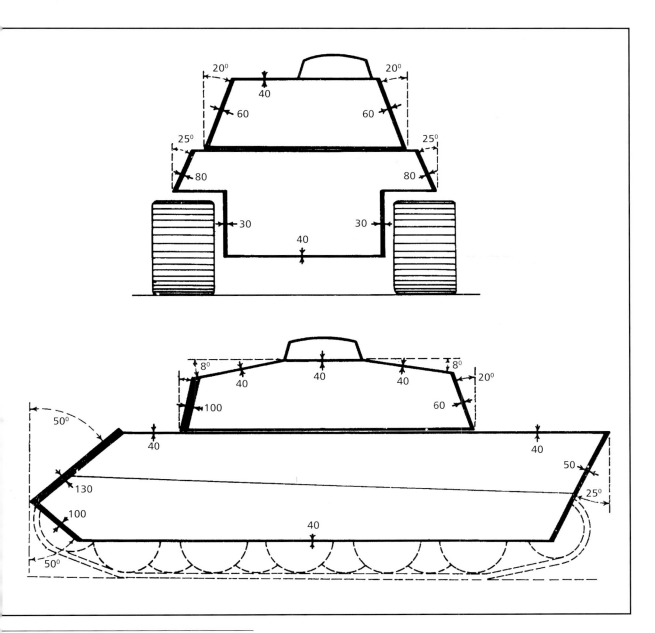

Armament

The main armament carried by the Tiger II, the 8.8cm KwK 43 L/71, was the most potent gun installed on any of the World War Two German tanks. It was a Krupp gun with its origins dating from the spring of 1941. At that time the intended replacement for the original 8.8cm anti-aircraft gun series was demonstrating signs of technical trouble. This was the 8.8cm Flak 41, designed as cover against being without a gun capable of tackling faster and higher-flying Allied bombers, Krupp of Essen was awarded a contract to develop an 'insurance' design.

Krupp decided not to just develop an anti-aircraft gun, but anti-tank and tank versions as well. The project name became *Gerät 42*. It was hoped that prototypes would be ready for the spring of 1943. By then, higher-flying Allied bombers had demonstrated that something even more advanced would soon be needed to reach them, so the anti-aircraft aspect of the *Gerät 42* was carried to other solutions, leaving Krupp to concentrate on the tank and anti-tank variants.

Above:
Armour protection on Tiger II was very substantial but at a cost to performance. The above diagram shows plating thickness on a standard production Henschel vehicle.

By late 1943 the *Gerät 42* had been developed into the *8.8cm PanzerabwehrKanone 43* (and the 8.8 cm PaK 43/41 hybrid) and the *8.8cm KampfwagenKanone 43 L/71*. Both guns shared the same ballistics and ammunition, although the tank gun differed mechanically by having the two recoil cylinders mounted over the two-piece barrel (examples for the Porsche turret had a one-piece barrel). The overall length was 71.6 calibres, enabling the gun to fire a standard armour-piercing projectile at a muzzle velocity of 3,280.8ft/sec (1,000m/sec). Range tests demonstrated the projectile could penetrate 5.48in (139mm) of armour set at 30° at 2,187yd (2,000m).

In the Tiger II turret the barrel could travel through a full 360° traverse and the elevation limits were from –7.4° to +15°. At one stage it was proposed that a 105 mm gun would utilise much the same mounting as for the KwK 43 but it never happened.

The rounds fired from the 8.8cm KwK 43 utilised much the same projectiles as for the KwK 36 but combined with a more powerful and larger propellant charge in a longer case. The ammunition types available for the KwK 43 included the following:

Projectile weight	Muzzle velocity	Type
8.8cm PanzergranatePatrone 40/43 KwK 43		
16.03lb (7.27kg)	3,707.3ft/sec (1,130 m/sec)	armour-piercing
8.8cm PanzergranatePatrone 39-1 KwK 43		
22.01lb (10kg)	3,208.8ft/sec (1,000 m/sec)	armour-piercing
8.8cm SprenggranatePatrone KwK 43		
21.03lb (43 9.54kg)	2,296.6ft/sec (700 m/sec)	high explosive
8.8cm PanzergranatePatrone 39/43 KwK 43		
16.86lb (7.65kg)	1,968.5ft/sec (600 m/sec)	hollow charge

In each case the KwK 43 suffix denoted that the primers were fired electrically, as with the KwK 36. Also as with the KwK 36, the main types encountered for the KwK 43 were the armour-piercing *8.8cm PanzergranatePatrone 39-1 KwK 43* and the high-explosive 8.8cm *SprenggranatePatrone 43 KwK 43*, usually in a mix of half and half. By the time the KwK 43 appeared the stocks of the tungsten-cored projectiles for the *8.8cm PanzergranatePatrone*

40/43 KwK 43 must have been almost exhausted and the few involved were probably remainders from KwK 36 production.

The shaped-charge *8.8cm PanzergranatePatrone 39/43 KwK 43* was rarely used as its low velocity meant it was too prone to environmental influences and therefore too inaccurate for armoured warfare. In addition the on-target result could be unpredictable as the projectile spin could disrupt the armour-penetrating, high-temperature jet that was the shaped charge's main asset.

On the Tiger II the turret bulged beyond the dimensions of the turret ring to provide stowage space for 22 rounds of 8.8cm ready-use ammunition, 11 each side of the breech recoil area. As the official combat load was 72 rounds, the rest were stored horizontally around the turntable floor and hull sides. Provision was made

Above:

A captured production Tiger II with a Henschel turret. Note the position for the ball-mounted machine gun and the Notek blackout headlamp. *(TM)*

to at least partially protect the rounds carried in .79in (20mm) thick steel panniers. It appears that up to a further eight rounds or so were also carried wherever space could be found.

Fire control on the Tiger II was much the same as for the Tiger I, the same methods and sighting systems being carried over.

Other Guns

Once again, the two machine guns carried by the Tiger, a turret co-axial gun and the bow machine gun, were the 7.92mm MG34. The bow machine gun was located behind a forged-steel hemispherical ball mounting. A virtual fixture was a third machine gun, a 7.92 mm MG42 on a *Fliegerabwehrschussgerät* (air-defence ring mounting) on the commander's cupola. A total of 5,850 rounds of 7.92mm ammunition was carried in belts of 150 rounds.

At least one 9mm MP38 or MP40 sub-machine gun was carried in each vehicle for dismounted use The official ammunition allotment for one sub-machine gun was 192 rounds for loading into six magazines.

A novel and almost universal fixture located in the Tiger II turret roof was a defensive innovation known as the *Nähverteidigungswaffe*. This was a short-barrelled, breech-loaded mortar that could be traversed 360^0 and launch smoke-screen cartridges. It could also be used to launch anti-personnel fragmentation grenades that detonated close to the vehicle to counter enemy infantry tank-killer squads.

Right:
On a training exercise, the crew of this PzKpfw VI Ausf E Tiger take a break. The numeral on the turret side ends with 1 denoting that it is the tank of a company commander. Note the turret has been coated with Zimmerit, anti-magnetic mine paste, before the camouflage paint was applied. *(TM)*

CHAPTER SEVEN

VARIANTS – TIGER II

Almost as soon as the first Tiger IIs appeared they became the subject of much planning for future vehicles. Apart from the *Jadgtiger*, few of these projects ever came anywhere near the hardware stage.

Almost as soon as the first Tiger IIs appeared they became the subject of much planning for future vehicles. Apart from the *Jadgtiger* (of which more below), few of these projects ever came anywhere near the hardware stage as after about August 1944 the industrial and transport infrastructure of the Third Reich was crumbling. Designers might have drawn up plans and all manner of mock-ups might have been built but there was no way their efforts would ever see the full light of day.

Mention must be made of the *Panzerbefehlswagen* command vehicle version of the Tiger II. Examples of these were manufactured from August 1944 onwards although it appears that no special SdKfz number was applied. The main radio installation was the usual *FuSprGer 5* radio installation plus the *FuSprGer 8*, the standard divisional level radio link within Panzer formations. It seems unlikely that many were provided with ground-to-air radios. As with the Tiger I command vehicles, the space required by the extra radio was acquired at the expense of ammunition stowage but no figures can be found.

Jagdtiger

As the most powerful combat vehicle to see action up till 1945, the *Jagdtiger* is deserving of a study of its own. It had its origins during early 1943 when a requirement was issued to field an anti-tank equipment capable of defeating anything the Allies were likely to field for years ahead. The result was a series of towed and self-propelled 128mm guns, one of which was selected for mounting in an armoured superstructure on a lengthened Tiger II hull Mock-ups were ready by October 1943 but a decision to employ a Porsche-designed lateral torsion bar suspension proved unsatisfactory and time was lost in reverting to a more conventional torsion bar system. Series production at the Nibelungwerke at St Valentin, Austria commenced during July 1944.

The *Jagdtiger* (SdKfz 186) was armed with the 12.8cm PaK 80 L/55 gun firing an armour-piercing projectile weighing 58.08lb (26.4kgs) at a muzzle velocity of 2,887ft/sec (880m/sec). It could defeat 5.63in (143mm) of armour at 1,093.6yd (1,000m) so it could eliminate

Above:
This *Jagdtiger* was captured intact in 1945 at Obernephen, Germany. The vehicle carries the number X7 and is part of sPzAbt. 512. *(TM)*

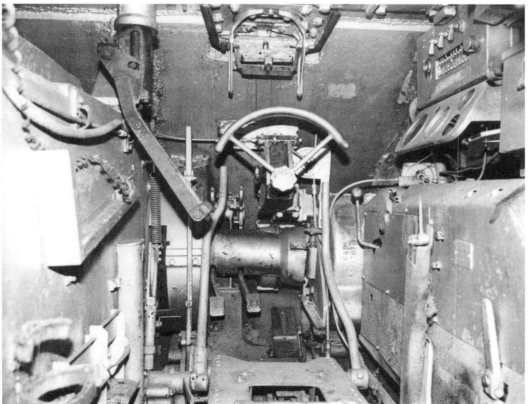

Left:
The driver's position in the *Jagdtiger* was a more cramped space than on the Tiger. Note the gearbox is now encased, and the one-third segment steering wheel. *(TM)*

Right:
Jagdpanzer VI,
(SdKfz 186) *Jagdtiger*,
mounted a powerful
12.8cm PaK44 L/55
gun and was a
formidable vehicle if
met on the battlefield,
easily eliminating
enemy tanks. The
Jagdtiger weighed 70
tons (71,122.9kgs) but
suffered from poor
performance as it was
powered by the same
engine as the 45-ton
(45,721.87kgs) Panther.

Right:
Developed from
Porsche's original
prototype for the
Tiger, VK4501(P),
a production run of 90
chassis were completed
as *Jagdpanzer Tiger (P)
Ferdinand* (later
Elefant) SdKfz 184s.
As with the original
they were powered by
two V-12 Maybach
HL 120 TR water-cooled
petrol engines with
Siemens electric-drive
units. The *Elefant* was
armed with a 8.8cm
PaK43/2 L/71 gun.
From 1943, two
heavy anti-tank
battalions were
equipped with them in
Russia. The surviving
Elefants were then
deployed in Italy,
1944. *(TM)*

any Allied tank then fielded, as well as any tank that might appear for the years after 1945. Barrel traverse was limited to 10° each side, with elevation from -7.5° to +15°. The usual 7.92mm MG34 machine gun was installed in a ball mounting at the hull front and a 7.92mm MG42 was mounted on the roof next to the commander's hatch.

The box-shaped superstructure, supplied by the Eisenwerke Oberdonau at Linz, had armour 9.85in (250mm) thick at the front and 3.15in (80mm) thick at the sides. The result was that the *Jagdtiger* had a combat weight of over 68.9 tons (69,999.2kgs) but was still powered by the V-12 Maybach 700hp engine and drive train as used with the late-production Tiger I. The *Jagdtiger* was thus as under-powered as the Tiger II and suffered from the same mobility limitations.

Fortunately for the Allies, *Jagdtiger* production was severely curtailed by the usual combination of supply delays plus, during 1944 a decision to convert the production line for other more pressing priorities. However, production continued until March 1945, by which time 79 had been completed.

Others

Among the many projects involving the Tiger II only one (other than the *Jagdtiger*) came anywhere near completion. This was a self-propelled artillery project designated the *17cm K44 (Sf)/GW VI* or *Gerät 809*, more generally known as the *Grille* (Cricket). This was meant to be one of a series of self-propelled artillery platforms based on a much modified and lengthened Tiger II hull and suspension. The artillery piece would be lowered to the ground for firing, although some limited-traverse firings could be made while still on the chassis. Included in the series were versions carrying 210, 305 or 420 mm howitzers or numerous types of large-calibre, smooth-bore mortars.

For the *Grille* role the number of axles each side was increased to at least 11. The projected combat weight was 57.1 tons (57,999.3kgs) so the well-tried V-12 Maybach 700hp engine was to have been retained. One prototype, without the gun, was delivered to the proving grounds at Sennelager just before the Allies arrived in 1945.

Both pages:
Three of the many projects for a self-propelled artillery weapon based on the Tiger II chassis. Originally designated *17cm K44 (sp) GW VI* or *Gërat 809*, the project was generally known as *Grille* (Cricket). It was to have been powered by the V-12 Maybach 700hp engine. Only one protoype chassis (without gun) was built by May 1945.

One other artillery-related Tiger II involved using two turretless Tiger II chassis as the two load-carrying components that were meant to carry a 28cm K 5(E) railway gun slung between them, the gun being broken down into components such as the barrel, cradle etc. This project, known as the *K 5 Eisenbahn Runden Feld*, was supposed to transport the gun between stretches of damaged track or around blocked railway tunnels. Considerable resources were devoted to this unlikely project but nothing transpired.

PzKpfw VI Ausf B TIGER II
1:35 scale

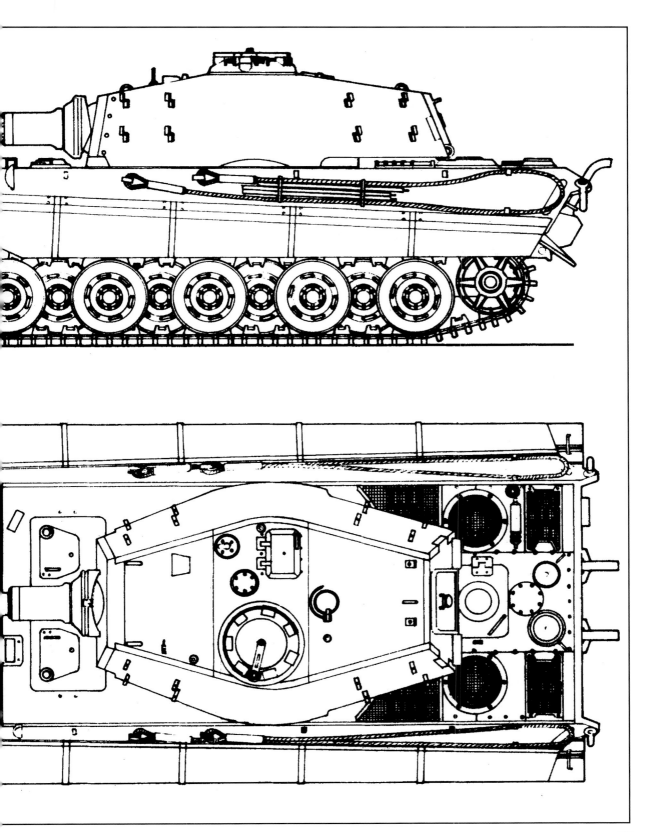

CHAPTER EIGHT

OPERATIONS & MARKINGS

Tiger I or II battalions operated independently under corps control, often in detachments as small as four or five tanks. They were difficult opponents to neutralise but the Allies discovered they were not invulnerable.

As a general rule Tiger I or II units were organised into heavy tank battalions (*schwere Panzerabteilungen*) operating under local corps control as the corps commander thought fit. When operating as a battalion, the tanks were organised into three companies, each with a complement of 14 tanks. The battalion headquarters company had a further three tanks so the full complement of Tigers was 45. Each company was sub-divided into three platoons, each with four tanks, the other two being held at company level.

In addition to the above the battalion had a headquarters unit and a support company devoted to keeping the tanks operational and supplied. Total personnel strength for the complete battalion was 27 officers, 216 NCOs and 406 unranked soldiers.

Although Tiger I or II battalions usually operated independently under corps control, often in detachments as small as four or five tanks, by 1945 some Tiger I battalions had been integrated into three *Waffen SS* Panzer divisions (*1st SS Pz Div. Leibstandarte Adolf Hitler, 2nd SS Pz Div. Das Reich* and *3rd SS Pz Div. Totenkopf*) and one *Wehrmacht* division (*Grossdeutschland*).

Action

The introduction of the Tiger I to combat had unfortunate results, for the first unit equipped, a platoon of the 502 *schwere Panzerabteilung*, was rushed ill-prepared into combat on a sector of the Leningrad front in August 1942. The platoon was forced to advance along a narrow approach where it was subjected to the usual Soviet defensive practice of aiming everything available, including heavy artillery, at tank targets,. The platoon suffered accordingly and some Tiger Is fell into Soviet hands for subsequent examination. Thus when Tiger Is were sent to Tunisia in 1943 the Allies had a good idea of what to expect so the combat impact of the Tiger I was somewhat less than it might have been. Even so, the presence of a few Tiger tanks was often enough to influence an armoured encounter to German advantage.

The Allies soon learned that the Tiger I was virtually invulnerable to their existing anti-tank measures – until they learned where the weak points were. The tank and anti-tank guns then in service (1943) could not penetrate the

Above:
A PzKpfw VI Tiger I in the foothills of the Italian Alps. *(TM)*

Left:
A damaged Tiger I awaits assistance from a *Bergepanzer IV* on a road in France, 1944. The tank is in transit: note the covers over the main gun muzzle brake and the ball-mounted hull machine gun. *(TM)*

Above:
A captured Tiger I
at Djebel Djaffa,
Tunisia, fitted with
Schnorkel deep water
equipment. *(TM)*

Left:
Tiger Is in the foothills
of the Italian Alps,
1944. Note the
covers on the main
gun and the hull
machine gun. *(TM)*

Right:
A *Zimmerit*-coated
Tiger II has been
repainted in a
late-war *Panzerwaffe*
camouflage scheme.
The vehicle is fitted
with a Henschel
turret and carries
the markings of
*1st Waffen SS
PanzerKorps*. *(RG/TM)*

Right:
Restored by and on
display at the Tank
Museum, Bovington,
Dorset, England, is
this PzKpfw VI Ausf E
Tiger I. *(RG/TM)*

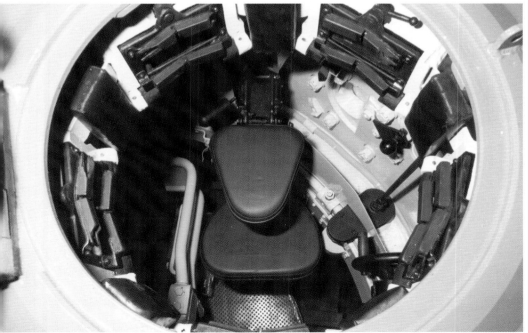

Left:
A view from the top of the cupola showing the commander's two-position seat. Note also the five vision ports fitted with *Ersatzgläser* blocks. *(RG/TM)*

Above:
The letter J on the rear turret stowage bins on this Tiger I is probably the first letter of the battalion commander's surname – a common practice in the *Panzerwaffe*. *(RG/TM)*

Right:
A Tiger II with Henschel turret displayed at the Panzer Museum, München, Germany.

Tiger I's thick armour but by 1944 some hastily introduced, larger-calibre guns could make an impression. The Allies soon came to appreciate that the Tigers could pick off their tanks at extreme combat ranges where they could not retaliate. They were forced to learn how to employ cover to 'stalk' their prey and fire at the more vulnerable side armour. When the Tiger II appeared the same procedures applied.

Two defensive measures became available from 1943 onwards that did much to reduce the usual invulnerability of the Tigers. One was the British fighter-bomber (usually the Typhoon) launching 3in (76.2mm) rockets. Launched in salvos, these rockets and their 60lb (27.2kg) high-explosive warheads could inflict devastating damage to the Tiger I or II. The rockets relied mainly on the sheer shattering effect of the impacting warhead. This could be sufficient to rupture welded joints, knock the turret off its bearings, or at least damage the tracks, vision devices and other items. The

rockets also had the advantage that they could impact on the relatively light top armour.

The second weapon was the shoulder-launched shaped charge. The US-produced Bazooka entered service, firing 2.36in (60mm) rockets, during 1943 and the British PIAT (Portable Infantry Anti-Tank) spigot mortar entered service at around the same time. Both fired projectiles with cone-shaped charges that produced a high-temperature jet that burned its way through thick armour. While the frontal armour of the Tiger I and II was usually proof against such attack, the hull sides were not. Even the Tiger II was vulnerable to such attacks so the point had been reached where every foot soldier could knock out an armoured vehicle the size of the Tiger II. The problem for foot soldiers was that they had to get dangerously close to their target to do so.

The Tiger I was originally intended to be a *Durchbruchwagen*. By the time it entered service it was a battle tank and by 1945 it was no longer

Above:
A PzKpfw VI Ausf E with *Zimmerit* anti-mine paste carries the markings of the *1st SS Panzer Korps. (HW)*

Tiger-Abteilungen (Battalions)

Panzer-Abteilung 501

Panzer-Abteilung 501
schwere (heavy) tactical mark

Panzer-Abteilung 502 Mammut
to late 1942

Panzer-Abteilung 502
from late 1942

Panzer-Abteilung 502
variant

Panzer-Abteilung 503

Panzer-Abteilung 504

Panzer-Abteilung 504

Panzer-Abteilung 504

Tiger-Abteilungen (Battalions)

Panzer-Abteilung 505

Panzer-Abteilung 506

Panzer-Abteilung 506

Panzer-Abteilung 507

Panzer-Abteilung 508

Panzer-Abteilung 509

Panzerjäger Abteilung 654
"N" for Major Noak, battalion commander

National Insignia 1942-1945 (Standard centre, variants left and right)

Above:
Detail showing the smoke cannister dischargers on the side of an Ausf E turret. Note the tiger emblem of *Panzer-Abteilung 501* and a member of the crew's name. *(TM)*

Right:
A Tiger I on display in Moscow at the end of hostilities. Note the non-standard stowage bin on the turret side. The insignia on the back of the turret is the outline of a *Mammut* (Mammoth) of *Panzer-Abteilung 502*. *(TM)*

Above:
The tiger for *Panzer-Abteilung 501* and the tactical mark for *schwere* (heavy) tank battalions. *(TM)*

even that. The vehicles' poor tactical mobility and slow reaction times once in action meant that Allied tanks could overcome them by sheer weight of numbers and better tactical mobility. By 1945 the Tigers were purely defensive vehicles, rendered largely immobile due to an ever-increasing fuel shortage throughout what was left of the Third Reich. They became little more than mobile strongpoints but even in that role they proved to be superb combat machines.

Markings

With Tigers organised as heavy tank battalions and held at corps or army level to reinforce other units as situations dictated, this led to the units developing distinct insignia which has been well identified over the years.

Due to the movements of the units between different divisions and fronts a wide variety of camouflage colours and tank turret numerals (also referred to as the tank's call sign) occurred,

with the battalion signs often appearing on the support vehicles only.

With its classic stalking tiger, sPzAbt 501 was the first unit to be sent to North Africa. Vehicles also displayed an S (for *schwere* – heavy tank unit) inside a red Panzer rhomboid. Turret numerals were the standard three-digit system in red with white outlines with all markings carried also by the battalion's PzKpfw IIIs.

A mammoth (*Mammut*) was used on the rear of the turret (a reference to the size of these vehicles) on sPzAbt 502's tanks. Due to the early use of 502's Tigers on the Eastern Front they took to the battlefield in dark grey. With winter the tanks were repainted white, covering markings and the three-digit turret numerals, though some vehicles had a single turret numeral reapplied in red.

Panzer Abteilung 503 saw action at Kursk and by late 1943 was operating as part of *Panzer Regiment Bake*, which changed its three-digit turret numerals to a single company-denoting digit. The battalion saw out hostilities in the East by which time it had been renamed

Panzer Divisions - Waffen SS.

1942

Kursk

1943-45

Leibstandarte SS Adolf Hitler

1942-45

Kursk

1944

Das Reich

Hitlerjugend

1942-45

Kursk

Kursk

Totenkopf

1944

Götz von Berlichingen

1942

1943-45

Nordland

Panzer Division signs, 1943-1945

10th Panzer Division

14th Panzer Division

60th Panzer Division
(Feldherrnhalle)

Grossdeutschland

Grossdeutschland
variant

Grossdeutschland
variant

24th Panzer Division

24th Panzer Division

24th Panzer Division
variant

25th Panzer Division

25th Panzer Division
variant

25th Panzer Division
variant

Above:
Loading ammunition from an SdKfz 252 halftrack *munnitions-panzer* to a Tiger I. The *Zimmerit* coated tank displays the battalion mark for *Panzer-Abteilung 507.* (TM)

Right:
Taken from the pages of *Signal*, Hitler's propoganda magazine, shows tank crews relaxing in the Tunisian desert. The tanks identifying number finishes with the numeral one, denoting that it is the mount for a company commander. (TM)

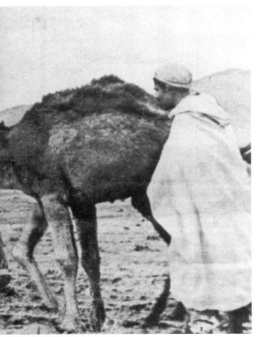

sPzAbt. Feldherrnhalle and was attached *Panzer Grenadier Division Feldherrnhalle*.

The second unit to be sent to North Africa was the first company of sPzAbt 504, the second company being stationed in Sicily. Each one had a company mark of a white rhomboid with a red stripe near its front edge – the numeral one or two denoting the company. The battalion mark was only applied to the support vehicles whilst the Tunisian company did not apply turret numerals.

The battalion finished the war in Italy as part of *17th SS Panzer Grenadier Division Götz von Berlichingen*.

The turret-placed charging knight of *sPzAbt 505* replaced an earlier stencil of a charging bull positioned next to the driver's vision slit. Turret numerals were initially the standard three-digit red with white outline, in some instances this was replaced with the unusual marking of a yellow band around the main armament's recuperator housing onto which black numerals were applied. The battalion ended the war attached to the *24th* and *25th Panzer Divisionen* in East Prussia.

The company tanks of sPzAbt 506 were individually numbered from one to 14 in white numerals until after Operation 'Market Garden' when numerals changed to the three-digit system. The battalion mark appeared on Tiger Is but not Tiger IIs, however all tanks carried a 3in (9.8cm) yellow circle containing a white cross.

Battalions 507, 508 and 509 all carried three-digit numerals but treated in different styles. PzAbt 507's company numeral was 50% bigger than the other two whilst 508's was in outline and one third as big again as the solid platoon and tank number.

The *Waffen SS* had Tiger battalions integrated into divisions and companies attached *SS Panzer Grenadiers*. The *Leibstandarte Adolf Hitler* had one company, numbered 13th, hence the turret numeral consisting of a 13 followed by a smaller identifying tank number. *Das Reich's* company carried a two-digit tank number (platoon and vehicle) prefixed by an S for *schwerer* (heavy). Company staff vehicles had the turret markings S01 and S02. The *Totenkopf* Tigers were organised as a company and carried the mark of a white gnome.

The *Waffen SS* had three Tiger battalions (sSSPzAbt 101, 102 and 103) attached to *1st SS Panzer Korps* whose unit mark was two crossed keys, not unlike *Hitlerjugend*, to whom they had a close association, sSSPzAbt 101 being attached to *Hitlerjugend* later in the war.

Turret numeral usage cross-section

1st SS Panzer Korps

Das Reich"Gnome"

Leibstandarte Adolf Hitler
turret numerals

Das Reich
turret numerals

Three-digit numeral system,
company, platoon, vehicle

Panzer Abteilung 502
three-digit numbering, 1942

Panzer Abteilung 502
single-digit numbering, Winter 1942-43

Panzer Abteilung 504
three-digit numbering, Italy 1944

© 2003 Nigel Pell.

Panzer Division signs, 1943-1945

sPzAbt 505
three-digit numbering on main armament
recuperator housing

Panzer Abteilung 506
individual tank numbering,
Eastern Front 1943

Panzer Abteilung 506
individual tank numbering,
Eastern Front 1943

Panzer Abteilung 507
three-digit numbering, 1944

Panzer Abteilung 508
three-digit numbering, 1944

Turret Numbers, colour and outline variations

© 2003 Nigel Pell.

Above: Every old tank has its use. *(TM)*